Elementary
Rheology

p. 141 for

Mirror something of swing plate attached with something and add something in

read ...

Mirror something of swing plate attached with something and something and something something

p. 131 for

p. 131 for

following treatment can be applied only when θ ≠ not very small.

read

following treatment can be applied only when θ ≠ not very small.

ELEMENTARY RHEOLOGY

ERRATA

p. 35: for

a stirrer consisting of a *hold* plate attached to a metal rod and timed another

read

a stirrer consisting of a holed plate attached to a metal rod and timed another

p. 122: for

$$\frac{\sigma}{\sigma_r} = \left(\frac{\varepsilon}{\varepsilon_r}\right)^{\mu T}\left(\frac{\dot{\varepsilon}}{\dot{\varepsilon}_r}\right)^{pT/T}$$

read

$$\frac{\sigma}{\sigma_r} = \left(\frac{\varepsilon}{\varepsilon_r}\right)^{\mu T}\left(\frac{\dot{\varepsilon}}{\dot{\varepsilon}_r}\right)^{pT/T_r}$$

p. 131: for

following treatment can be applied only when L is not very small.

read

following treatment can be applied only when 1 is not very small.

Elementary Rheology

G W Scott Blair

1969

Academic Press
London and New York

Academic Press Inc. (London) Ltd
Berkeley Square House
Berkeley Square
London W1X 6BA

U.S. Edition published by
Academic Press Inc.
111 Fifth Avenue
New York New York 10003

Library of Congress Catalog Card Number: 69–16498

Printed in Great Britain by
Butler and Tanner Ltd, Frome and London

Dedicated to
M.F.S.B., who has lived in
an atmosphere of Rheology
for over forty years

Preface

This is a book on Rheology not intended for rheologists. I have been asked to write it by two groups of people. First, there are research workers who need to have some ideas concerning what rheology is about, either because they have a rheologist in their team; or, more often, because they themselves need to do some kind of tests of consistency and have no idea how to set about it. The second group consists of students who have no opportunity, or have not yet had an opportunity, of attending a course on rheology at some college or university. It is assumed that neither group has more than a very elementary knowledge of mathematics. It is hoped that this book may inspire a few to go further into the subject and perhaps even to become rheologists. For this, more advanced mathematics is essential. To help such people, an appendix is given which lists the most easily available books on the subject, with brief appraisals of their standards and subject-matter.

Rather a large proportion of this small book is concerned with biological applications. This is because I believe that, just as the last twenty years have seen the greatest rheological advances in the field of macromolecules, the present trend is towards biology and medicine.

As Co-Editor in Chief of the journal *Biorheology*, I have been conscious of the large increase in the number of submitted papers in recent times; and my old friend and fellow Editor in Chief, Prof. A. L. Copley, has started and is President of a newly-founded International Society of Hemorheology. It was founded because of the insistence of our medical colleagues that rheology can play an important part in the study of thromboses and of the haemophilic diseases.

There is also considerable interest in trying to link the assessments of quality of materials, as judged by experts handling them, with the results of rheological tests, so I have included a chapter on "Psycho-rheology".

I have preferred to write quite a large number of very short chapters. This is deliberate, because I hope that one possible use of the book will be to help the research worker who, coming across rheological terminology in a particular field, will want quickly to be able to get some idea of what it is all about. This can be done in a very short time by reading just one chapter.

I have explained the meaning of as many rheological terms as possible, though not always with a precise definition. This is because nomenclature is not yet fully agreed on among rheologists themselves. Professor Reiner and I have recently published, with the help of many of the leading rheologists, a list of terms with formal definitions, but this is not an official document and we quite expect it to be improved and amended. To help the reader, when a new term is defined or explained, it is printed in *italics* and may easily be found from the subject index.

References to published papers have been limited to those likely to be reasonably understandable to the beginner and also fairly easily available. Even very important papers in obscure journals or containing difficult mathematics are not included. When a reference is included, the author's name is given, without initials, followed by the date in parentheses. The initials are to be found in the list of references. When an author's work is mentioned but not listed among the references, initials are given, but the date is given only if it has special significance.

It was suggested to me that I should include the calculations of the equations of the best-known types of viscometer and also give equations (without calculations) for some of the more complex instruments. This information is to be found in many other books, but it was pointed out to me that the reader may not want to consult other books or may not find it easy to do so; and for this reason such calculations, and a few equations, are given as an appendix. Naturally, nothing like all available methods could be included.

It may be felt that I have quoted too much of my own work in this book. This is not because I am under any delusions that my work is better than that of other rheologists; but simply that, in a book of this kind, broad principles must be illustrated by examples and I have taken many of these from my own work simply because I know it better than I know that of other people.

There is one large group of materials whose properties were much studied before the name "rheology" was invented: the metals.

Although metals and non-metals sometimes show surprisingly similar rheological behaviour, the field of metal rheology is highly specialized and it is a field in which I have no personal experience. I therefore persuaded my good friend Mr A. Graham, who is a well-known metal rheologist, to write a chapter on metals, which is given as the first appendix to the book. I am also much indebted to him and also to my friend Dr Philip Sherman for reading the whole text of the book before I sent it to the publishers.

Finally, I would thank Mrs D. Steer who typed the manuscript for me. I feel sure that she will now distinguish between the "stresses and strains" involved in such a task!

G. W. Scott Blair
Grist Cottage
Iffley
Oxford
January 1969

Contents

1/Introduction

"What is rheology all about?" How often have I been asked this question, I wonder, during my forty or so years as a practising rheologist.

The definition, as originally agreed, is simple: "Rheology is the study of the deformation and flow of matter." The term was invented by the late Prof. E. C. Bingham, of Lafayette College, Easton (Pa.), U.S.A., on the advice of his Professor of Classics and was accepted when the (American) Society of Rheology was founded in 1929.

I was fortunate enough to be present at the first Conference, held in Washington (D.C.) at the end of that year. By common consent, the definition excluded studies of the flow of electrons and of heat and it was agreed that rheologists were interested in the properties and constitution of the "matter" under investigation so that pure hydro- and aero-dynamics and the classical theory of elasticity would not be included in spite of the definition.

In recent times, as we shall see later, fluid mechanics has become involved in the study, not only of flow, but also of the complex properties of some flowing materials. Such studies form a link between hydrodynamics and rheology.

Professor Reiner of Haifa, who was a moving spirit in the founding of the American Society and is almost certainly the oldest practising rheologist, has pointed out that, since flow is a type of deformation, the definition is tautologous. In our recent list of rheological definitions (Eirich 1967) we have modified the definition to read "the study of the deformation of materials, including flow".

Of course much rheology was done before 1929, although the term was not yet introduced. In fact the root "rheo" (Greek: flow) had been used by a few earlier workers but it is unlikely that Bingham knew this in 1928.

The Washington Conference was quite a small one; but one of its most striking features was the wide range of interest of the participants. The Abstracts in the first number of the long-since defunct "Journal of Rheology" included "asphalt, pitch, ceramic materials, lime, cement, lubricants, paint,

1

oils, varnish, lacquers and plastics, rubber"; and the biological sciences were also soon to be included in rheological programmes.

Today, there are Societies or less formal groups of rheologists in many countries; and the Fifth International Congress on Rheology is planned to be held in Kyoto (Japan) in 1968. The Proceedings of the Fourth Conference (Providence, Rhode Island, U.S.A.), held in 1963, filled four quite large volumes.

An international journal, "Rheologica Acta" (published in Germany) deals with the subject as a whole and another international journal specializes in "Biorheology". Of course, many other journals publish papers on rheology as well as these.

One of the most important activities of the national societies, second only to their function of making personal contacts, is to establish an agreed terminology. We may define any word to mean anything we wish so long as we are consistent but, in technical subjects such as rheology, an agreed nomenclature is essential.

There are two sorts of technical terms. First we have ordinary everyday words given a special connotation. This means that their "denotation", represented by the range of materials or behaviour, is reduced unless there is an overall increase in the size of the field to be covered (see Scott Blair 1950).

For example, in everyday English, "stress" and "strain" mean much the same thing. Most people would not know what was meant by such a statement as "there is no stress in this direction but only a considerable strain".

The rheologist uses the word "stress" to refer to a system of forces whereas "strain" refers solely to a change of size or shape. The "field" covered by each of these terms is thus reduced but the precision of meaning is increased. English is a particularly fortunate language for this kind of procedure because, being derived from so many sources, it has many words which are, in common use, almost synonyms. The scientist can use each of these synonyms for some special purpose.

The second type of term is deliberately invented, being derived generally from Greek or Latin.* When a rheologist discovers a new phenomenon, he often invents and defines such terms. ("Rheology" itself is, of course, a case of this.) Sometimes the inventor himself feels, after further experience, that his term should be given a wider or a narrower meaning (decreased or increased connotation). This is generally allowed: but, in modern times, it is usually dangerous for other rheologists to change the meaning of a term.

---

* The latest nuclear particle has a name ("tamed") derived from Welsh!

If this is done, readers of articles can never know (except approximately from the date of the article) which meaning is intended. We shall see later what confusion has been caused by this sort of change in the case of the term "rheopexy". It is, therefore, *very important indeed* that authors and editors of rheological papers be extremely exact in their use of technical terms and, in translating from one language to another, that the synonyms really do have exactly the same meaning in the two countries concerned.

Before closing this introductory chapter, two more pitfalls must be pointed out. The first is well illustrated by an anonymous remark quoted by Willets (1967)*: "Rheologists can be divided into two classes: the practical rheologists who observe the things that cannot be explained, and the theoretical rheologists who explain the things that cannot be observed." This is rather unkind but it does point out a very real danger. Most rheologists, whether full- or part-time, are concerned with how materials behave in practice, usually under rather large deformations and forces. But, in many cases, these large deformations and forces themselves change the properties of the material. The information got from tests which at all resemble the conditions under which the material is used is in terms of "processes" rather than "properties". Physical "properties", at above the quantum level, should not be changed by the process of measuring them. Such properties can be measured only when very "gentle" methods are used and these may well be of little practical interest. Later in this book we shall see how this dilemma recurs repeatedly in rheology.

The second pitfall is concerned with the correct use of mathematics. Since 1929, when the mathematics of rheology was within the range of most competent schoolboys, there has been a steady increase in the complexity of mathematical treatments. We have already said something about this in the preface in explaining why this book is deliberately written to include a minimum of mathematics. It would be completely wrong to belittle the enormous help, indeed the quite essential help, that mathematics gives to the rheologist. Nevertheless, Lord Rutherford is reported to have said: "It is as dangerous to let mathematics take charge of physics as to let an army run a government." In these days when so many of the world's governments are run openly or less obviously by armies, this has become a grave warning indeed! Mathematics is a form of logic. It is perhaps not too inexact to say that the mathematician can do anything that does not involve a contradiction. Physics, of which rheology is a part, is, on the contrary, concerned with the real world. Why the "real world" corresponds so closely to the mathe-

---

* I am told that this remark was made, originally about hydrodynamics, by my old Tutor, the late Sir Cyril Hinshelwood.

matician's world has long been a subject of debate among philosophers. But we shall see, in the course of this book, that there have been times when the mathematicians have put restrictions on the rheologists which were really not necessary. It must also be remembered that it is no "explanation" to the rheologist to tell him that some phenomenon occurs "because a particular component of the stress tensor is not zero". This leads only to the further question: "Why is it not zero?" *

This is not to say that we still live in Lord Kelvin's age, when the only real understanding of phenomena depended on being able to make models; but it does mean that you cannot predict how a complex material will behave by means of mathematics alone. This can be done only by experiments, or by some inductive theory derived from the results of experiments (even though the logic of induction is highly questionable!) or from a deductive theory which must always be checked by experiments. Most rheological work combines induction and deduction, though many rheologists tend to have a personal preference for one or other of these methods (you will probably guess, if you read the rest of this book, that I tend towards an inductive approach).

---

* For more advanced readers—I met a good example of this sort of thing many years ago when I wanted to find out the precise meaning of the terms "covariant" and "contravariant". I looked in all the textbooks I could find on tensors and matrices and the answer was always much the same: "a component is covariant when the indices are written as suffixes, e.g. p_{xy}, and contravariant when written with superfixes: p^{uv}". I finally got my explanation by asking a friend with more knowledge of mathematics than my own.

Recently, this matter has become quite important for rheologists, since A. S. Lodge has proposed a scheme of "rheology without tensors" which has greater flexibility for large strains than the usual tensor methods. He uses matrices which look like tensors to the uninitiated but do not, in fact, have all the properties of tensors. This involves non-orthogonal coordinates (i.e. not at right-angles) and some of the components of the matrices have to be contravariant.

Part I
Rheological Systems and Concepts

B

2/Laws and Equations. "Basic Equations". Elasticity

This is not the place to discuss at length the distinction between scientific laws, hypotheses and equations. So far as rheology is concerned, no very precise distinction is generally made; but the most fundamental equations which are the simplest and which, fortunately do hold for many real materials with a high degree of accuracy, are generally called "laws".

All branches of physics have such "laws" but rheology is fortunate in having quite a simple hierarchy of them. The equations which express these laws, I shall call "basic equations". The characteristics of a basic equation are that it is simple and can therefore form a basis for further amendments for more complex systems; and that it is obeyed with reasonable accuracy by a fairly large number of real materials. From the former requirement it follows that basic equations can generally be represented by some fairly simple model or process.

In this book, we are not discussing the early history of rheological experimentation. This has been done in my book "A Survey of General and Applied Rheology",* now unfortunately out of print. We will start at the point when rheology began to be quantitative, that is with Robert Hooke, who, in about 1660, hung long metal wires from the ceiling and, applying various loads, measured the height of the lower end from the floor. Only by so doing could he measure the very small extensions produced by loads not too large to break the wires. He also loaded coiled springs. (In the first book on rheology which I wrote in 1938, I spelt "Hook" without the final "e" and was criticized for so doing. In fact this is how he generally wrote his own name; but it has become customary to write "Hooke" and it would seem pedantic not to do so.)

Hooke was suspicious, perhaps rightly, of his fellow-scientists and it was not until 1676 that he published his "law" in anagram form, nor did he

---

* This book, published by Sir Isaac Pitman & Sons, London (2nd edn. 1949) may be obtained in microfilm or xerographic form from University Microfilms Ltd., 31 Alford Place, London, W.C.1.

finally interpret it until 1678. Mariotte independently discovered the same law in 1680.

Hooke's formulation was in Latin: "ut tensio sic vis" (as is the extension so is the force). In modern times, what this means is that, over a small range, the forces of attraction and repulsion between the atoms balance in such a way that, if the load is doubled the extension is doubled. This must, of course, refer to the *relative* extension (which we call "strain") since, if the wire were twice as long it would extend twice as far under the same load. Atoms cannot be pulled far apart without rupture and the simple definition of strain as $(1 - 1_0)/1_0$ (known as the Cauchy definition) is adequate for systems like most metal wires. (1_0 is the unloaded and 1 the loaded length of the wire.) Coiled springs can, of course, be stretched much further and, as every user of a spring-balance will know, Hooke's law still holds. This is because the atoms are not only being pulled apart but turned around with respect to one another. It is these "rotations" which add up to produce the large extensions; but Hooke, of course, did not appreciate this.

Unfortunately practical people are not always pulling wires in one direction, so, in the "Theory of Elasticity", the most general case has to be considered, i.e. that of a lump of material acted on by forces in any direction and strained in any direction. One simplification may be made: forces will be expressed "per unit area" and we can take a cube having sides 1 cm long, as representing our lump of matter. (Assumptions must also be made about the "continuity" of the cube, but these will not be considered here.)

Moreover, if the cube is standing on the bench and loaded vertically from above, following one of Newton's laws, the upward force of reaction from the bench must be equal and opposite to the impressed force; and this means that we need consider the forces on only three, and not all six of the sides of the cube. We will describe forces acting "normally" (i.e. at right-angles) to these faces as x, y and z forces.

Now all the forces acting on the x-face may be considered as made up of three parts, one part normal to the face, which we will call p_{xx} (or p_x for short) and two parts along the face, one in the y-direction (p_{xy}) and the other in the z-direction (p_{xz}). It would thus appear that all the forces acting on the cube could be described in terms of nine components. In fact, pairs of forces such as p_{xy} and p_{yx} are the same, and this reduces the number of components from nine to six: the three "normal" forces, p_x, p_y, p_z, and the three tangential, or shearing forces, p_{xy}, p_{xz}, p_{yz}. These components correctly called "tractions", together form what is known as "the stress tensor".

Tensors have many interesting and useful properties but they will not be considered in detail in this elementary book. Full-time rheologists and others who wish to understand more advanced books and papers must make themselves familiar at least with the basis of tensor theory.

Suffice it here to say that the components of the strain may also be described by a tensor, though this is slightly more complicated. All the forces (tractions) taken together, constitute the "state of stress"; likewise the strain tensor gives "the state of strain"—but rheologists often use the terms "stress" and "strain" to mean the individual components of the tensors.

Since Hooke's law tells us that stress is proportional to strain, their ratio is a constant. Each component of stress may be divided by each component of strain to give an *elastic modulus*, or dividing strains by stresses (the reciprocal) a *compliance*. In tensor theory, compliances are easier to deal with and it is clear that there should be 36 (6 × 6) of them: but there are two simplifications. First, the compliances themselves form a tensor and, like the stress and strain tensors, a number of pairs are found to be identical. This reduces the total possible number to 21. Secondly, most materials show some degree of "isotropy", e.g. a cube of wood differs in properties along and across the grain but the properties in the planes at right-angles across the grain are the same and this reduces the number to nine. If the material has the same properties in all directions (perfectly isotropic), we have only two: *Young's modulus*, for extensions (and generally the same value for compressions) and the *shear or rigidity modulus* for the tangential forces.

The reader should know the meaning of a few more technical terms. First, a property which has magnitude but no direction, such as an elastic modulus, is called a *scalar*. A traction, which has both magnitude and direction, is a type of *vector*. A tensor (like the stress and strain tensors) whose components require two suffixes, e.g. p_{xy}, is called a *second rank* or *second order* tensor. Each of the components of the tensor of compliances must have four suffixes: two for the traction and two for the component of strain. This is known as a *fourth rank tensor*. By analogy, vectors are sometimes called tensors of the first rank and scalars as tensors of zero rank.

There is some disagreement among rheologists as to whether deformations which are not completely "elastic", i.e. completely recovered immediately, or even gradually, after the load is removed, should be called "strains". Historically, there is much to be said for keeping the term "strain" solely for elastic deformations. But so often in practice it is hard to decide whether a deformation will recover if you wait long enough, or if you expose the sample to, say, heat or vibration, that most rheologists find it convenient to use the term for all deformations.

We have said that atoms cannot be pulled very far apart without rupture but we all know that there are many materials, like rubber, which can be extended to many times their original length and which recover when released. This phenomenon is known as *high elasticity* and in some cases high-elastic strains approximately obey Hooke's law. While this may be due to a structure like that of a coiled spring, in which energy is "stored", it is much more often produced by quite a different mechanism.

In rubber, for instance, the long-chain molecules can form all sorts of configurations: some coiled up—some elongated to a greater or lesser degree. But it is clear that there will be far more possible "coiled up" configurations than extended ones. Since the molecules are continually changing their configurations, so long as there is no stress on the rubber, the great majority will stay coiled up. If a strand of rubber is extended by force, most of the molecules are made to extend into much less "probable" shapes. When the load is removed, because of thermal agitation they will go back to the much more "probable" contracted formations and the strain will recover.

Probabilities are "multiplicative": this means that if the probability of an event A is 0·2 and of an independent event B is 0·3, the probability of both events happening will be 0·2 × 0·3 = 0·06. But physicists prefer to deal with entities that are additive. The logarithms of probabilities are, of course, additive, and these give a measure of a property known as "entropy". This is often described as "the degree of mixed-upness". The second law of thermodynamics tells us that the entropy of closed systems always tends to increase. Hence, when a stretched strand of rubber is released, in order to get "more mixed up", the long-chain molecules have, on the average, to contract and rubber-like high-elasticity is therefore sometimes called *entropy elasticity*. Of course Hooke's law does not always hold. When we come to consider power-equations, we shall find a modification of it. But it is one of the two fundamental basic equations of rheology and underlies the whole of the theory of elasticity.

Before closing this chapter, we should say a word about large strains. Suppose we have a wire 10 cm long and, on loading, with a load W, it extends to 11 cm. The strain, following Cauchy, would be 1/10 or 0·1. Now we double the load and (not worrying about thinning of the wire) the strain doubles—the extended length would then be 12 cm. But, starting at 11 cm and applying a load W should produce an extension of 1·1 cm, or a total length of 12·1 cm. Now clearly the strains should not depend on whether we consider the load as being applied in one or in two stages. To get over this difficulty, Hencky proposed that we add up the strains for each infinitesimal increment of stress. This gives as a definition of strain $\int_{l_0}^{l} dl/l = \ln(l/l_0)$.

(I hope that this little bit of elementary calculus will not worry the reader!) The principle is the same as that involved in defining the base of natural logarithms. It is the "law of compound interest", except that the interest is added to the capital continuously and not just once a year.

Although the Hencky formula is much to be preferred to the Cauchy for large strains, even the former has its disadvantages. It is still a matter for discussion among rheologists whether any formula for really large strains is entirely satisfactory.

3/Flow: Liquids and Solids

While the basic law of elasticity is that of Hooke, the corresponding law of flow derives from Isaac Newton. In his great "Principia", published in 1687 (though probably written somewhat earlier) he wrote:* "Hypothesis: that the resistance which arises from the lack of slipperiness of the parts of a liquid, other things being equal, is proportional to the velocity with which the parts of the liquid are separated from one another."

We now call "the lack of slipperiness", "viscosity". This is quite an old word and it is typical that it originally meant "stickiness", the term being derived from the Latin word for mistletoe. Physicists have given it a precise meaning. Before considering this precise meaning, we must return to the word "shear" which was introduced in Chapter 2. *Shear* is defined by Reiner and Scott Blair (*loc. cit.*) as "the change in angle between any two material lines in a deforming body". There are two principal types of shear: *simple shear* and *pure shear*. Simple shear is defined as "a laminar deformation parallel

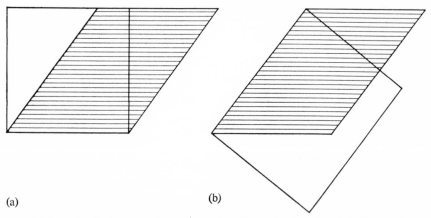

(a)   (b)

Fig. 3.1 Two simple shears producing a rotation (Note: for the sake of clarity, very large shears are shown; this produces a "stretching" of the square)

* Translation quoted from Reiner. "Deformation, Strain and Flow", see p. 142.

12

to a stationary plane". This is best pictured by what happens when a deck of cards is pushed sideways (see Fig. 3.1a). A deck of cards can be deformed only sideways. If the material has the same properties in all directions, it can be sheared again so that the face once more becomes square, cancelling the first shear. But it will be seen from Fig. 3.1b that in doing this, the figure has been rotated through an angle. We have already briefly mentioned these *rotations* in connection with the stretching of a coiled spring. They are characteristic of simple shear.

Rotation can be avoided if we put a cube of deformable material on a flat board between two parallel vertical plates arranged so that the cube cannot expand in one horizontal plane. If we then apply a force downwards, so as to compress the cube, it will expand correspondingly in the horizontal plane in which it is free. This constitutes a "pure shear". (A somewhat crude but simple way of remembering this distinction is that simple people don't always keep straight: pure people do.) We have said that the cube will expand "correspondingly" to the compression. If we take away the two vertical baffle plates the cube will normally expand equally in both planes. If our compression has produced no appreciable change of volume, the sideways expansion in each plane will be half of the compression. This is true of liquids in general. With solid materials the volume is often changed so that the sideways expansion ratio is less than half. This ratio is called *Poisson's ratio* (ν). (It has nothing to do with fish: Poisson was a French scientist!)

A material like cork or a sponge is really a mixture of a solid structure and air. When a cylinder of such a material is compressed, air is pushed out and the total volume may be so much reduced that there is virtually no sideways expansion. The Poisson's ratio of such a system is zero. Anisotropic materials, i.e. those having different properties in different directions, will have more than one Poisson's ratio, just as elastic materials in general have more than one elastic modulus.

Although not independent of the other constants so far discussed there is also the *bulk modulus* (sometimes also called the "compression modulus", though this is confusing, since it might refer to Young's modulus (E) in compression as opposed to the usual value in extension). The bulk modulus (K) is defined as "the modulus of volume expansion: the ratio of the isotropic stress to the relative change in volume". This need not, of course, be an expansion: a contraction is regarded as a negative expansion. "The isotropic stress" simply means that the specimen is being stressed equally in all three planes, or $p_x = p_y = p_z$.

The following simple equations relate these moduli to Poisson's ratio:

$$E = 2(1 + \nu)G \text{ when G is the shear modulus}$$

$$\nu = \frac{3K - 2G}{6K + 2G} \quad \text{or} \quad 3K(1{-}2\nu) = 2G(1 + \nu)$$

One more term should be defined before we see how the definition of viscosity fits into this picture: *Resilience* is a measure of the elastic energy stored by a body and is generally quoted as an energy per unit volume. (We shall be discussing dimensions later.)

In the case of solids, it is apparent that the situation is pretty complicated. In the case of liquids, it is much less so. There are two reasons for this. First, liquids are normally isotropic, which reduces the number of "properties" very greatly. Secondly, they are also generally incompressible, or at least any change of volume when the liquid is sheared can be ignored. This means that Poisson's ratio is a half and the equations given above are greatly simplified.

Hooke's law tells us that, for an elastic solid, the ratio of stress to shear (the shear modulus) is constant. Newton's law tells us that, for simple liquids (Newton was careful to say "other things being equal") the ratio of stress to *rate* of shear is constant. It is this ratio that we define as *viscosity* and the symbol η is now almost always used for it. So much for shear; but highly viscous liquids, such as certain bitumens, pitch, etc., can be extended in the form of rods. The property equivalent to Young's modulus in this case is called the *coefficient of viscous traction*. It follows that if Poisson's ratio is half, this must always be three times as great as the viscosity and Trouton (1906) long ago showed experimentally that this is true for Newtonian, or almost Newtonian materials. The reciprocal of viscosity is often known as *fluidity* and, especially in relation to chemical constitution, it is sometimes simpler to use than is viscosity. If we take into account the (usually small) changes of volume involved when a liquid is sheared, we must also consider the rate at which the volume change takes place and this involves a second viscosity, but this hardly comes within the scope of elementary rheology.

It was many years after 1687 before any practical use was made of Newton's "hypothesis". In the nineteenth century, experiments were done, especially in France, to establish the law relating rate of flow (V as volume/sec) of a liquid through a pipe (usually a long narrow tube) to the applied pressure or pressure difference (P), the radius of the tube (R) and its length (L). For some time, it was thought that V was proportional to the square of R. J. L. M. Poiseuille, who died in Paris almost exactly a hundred years ago, is generally regarded as the founder of Biorheology. He at first believed this same square law and explained some of the phenomena that he observed in the flow of blood in terms of it. Later, however, he very sensibly carried out many experiments on much simpler systems than blood and blood-vessels and studied the flow of liquids such as water and alcohol through long narrow straight cylindrical glass tubes. He found that V is proportional to P, inversely proportional to L and proportional, not to R^2, but to R^4. Unfortunately he took a long time to publish his results and, in the meantime G. Hagen, in Germany, though his experiments were less extensive, published what was essentially the same law. It is generally known as the "Poiseuille-Hagen law", though strictly the names should be reversed. (It is a good rule that when two workers discover the same law or equation independently, the names are joined by a hyphen; if two workers publish together an "and" is inserted. I believe it was Professor Reiner who first established this convention).

It was some years before it was noticed that the Poiseuille-Hagen equation follows directly from Newton's law, combined with a few fairly obvious boundary conditions. The calculation is very simple and is to be found in almost all rheology textbooks as well as in many books on general physics. To save the reader trouble, however, it is reproduced in Appendix 2.

There are many ways of measuring viscosity as well as the capillary tube viscometer, which has its disadvantages for systems that do not obey Newton's law. Some of them will be briefly discussed in Chapter 14.

There has been much discussion among rheologists as to whether the term "viscosity" should be used to describe the behaviour of systems that do not obey Newton's law, i.e. in which viscosity is not independent of shear-rate and stress. The term should certainly not be used for properties which do not have the dimensions of stress/shear-rate; though, as we shall see later, combined terms such as "relative viscosity", "specific viscosity" refer to properties that are not viscosities at all. If we want to discuss a ratio of stress to shear-rate that is not constant, the term "apparent viscosity" and the symbol η' is best used.

To return to Newtonian systems, their principal interest to rheologists lies in the variation of viscosity with changes in temperature and, in very special cases, with high hydrostatic pressures, though the latter hardly comes within the range of elementary rheology. The various theories of liquid structure, on which equations relating viscosity to absolute temperature (T) are based, are also outside the scope of this book. Suffice it to say that the general trend of thought has been to picture liquids rather as "degenerate solids" than as "condensed gases". Liquids certainly have a structure, but there are holes in the structure and the flow of the liquid depends on the transfer of the molecules by way of these holes. Eyring and his colleagues (see Glasstone, Laidler and Eyring 1941) long ago proposed the "theory of rate processes". This explains flow in terms very similar to those familiar as characterizing a simple chemical reaction. If we have two layers of molecules, one sliding past the other, "the motion of one layer with respect to another is assumed to involve the passage of a molecule from one equilibrium position to another such position in the same layer". This implies the presence of a "hole" and there must be a potential barrier requiring a certain energy on the part of the molecules to cross it. When not under stress, molecules whose thermal energy is great enough will cross these barriers but in statistically equal numbers in all directions. When a stress is applied, the barriers cease to be symmetrical and the liquid will flow (see Fig. 3.2). The need for "holes" has been questioned by J. D. Bernal, who proposes a much more difficult theory which is beyond the scope of this book.

Both these theories, and many modifications of them, lead, at least approximately, to a basic equation, first proposed quite empirically by de Guzmán in 1913 and later rediscovered a number of times, which gives a linear relation between $\ln \eta$ and $1/T$. This is generally known as "the Sheppard-Andrade equation", named after two of its principal exponents.

This equation holds with fair accuracy for many liquids, though strangely enough, not for water. Water is a much more complex liquid than might be supposed. Like all basic equations, this has been modified by the addition of further terms so as to give better agreement for certain liquids. The fact that the viscosity of liquids falls with a rise in temperature and does not increase, as is the case with gases, is evidence that there must be a structure that is broken down as the kinetic energy of the molecules increases. A *liquid* (not necessarily Newtonian) is defined as a system which behaves in this way (i.e. is not a gas) but which will flow, however slowly, under the smallest measurable pressures. As C. N. Hinshelwood has put it: "A liquid [has] a lattice so mobile under shear that it exists only as a time average. It might be likened to a flight of birds attempting to keep formation in a gale" (Hinshelwood 1952). P. W. Bridgman's classical work on the effect of very high isotropic pressures on the viscosity of liquid led to an equation

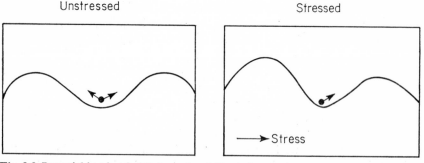

Fig. 3.2 Potential barriers in Unstressed and Stressed systems

relating viscosity to pressure which has the same form as the Sheppard-Andrade equation.

We will conclude this chapter with a note which has some historical interest. If Aristotle had not confused density with viscosity he might well have claimed priority over Newton and also to have foreseen the principles underlying Stokes' law for the fall of a sphere through a liquid (which will be discussed later).

Aristotle wrote:* "Now the medium causes a difference because it impedes the moving thing most of all if it is moving in the opposite direction, but in a secondary degree, even if it is at rest; and especially a medium that is not easily divided; i.e. a medium that is somewhat dense. A then, will move through B in time C, and through D, which is thinner, in time E (if the length of B is equal to D) in proportion to the density of the hindering body. For let B be water and D air; then by so much as air is thinner and more incorporeal than water, A will move through D faster than through B. Let the speed have the same ratio to the speed, then, that air has to water. Then if air is twice as thin, the body will traverse B in twice the time E. And always, by so much as the medium is more incorporeal and less resistant and more easily divided, the faster will be the movement."

---

* Quoted from W. D. Ross. "Aristotle" (5th. edn.), Methuen, London, 1949, p. 227.

4/Rheological Models of Complex Systems

There are many materials that flow, but for which the ratio of shear-stress to shear-rate (viscosity) is not a constant. (Newton would seem to have foreseen this in his definition: "other things being equal".) For some of these systems, however, there is one well-defined stress for each rate of shear, i.e. a single "apparent viscosity", the measurement of which can be repeated a number of times, whether the shear-rates used are rising or falling and this does not change when the system has rested for a reasonable time.

It will be clear that this definition is somewhat arbitrary. Suppose that a system has a structure that is broken down by shearing, so that the apparent viscosity falls as the shear-rate increases. If this structure is recovered so quickly that, before another experiment can be done, the original structure has been restored, the system will appear to be monotonic. But this depends on the rate at which we can do our experiments. For this reason, a few rheologists refuse to make this distinction, as we shall see when we come to define "thixotropy" in a later chapter. The great majority, however, accept the distinction because, in fact, there are very few known borderline cases and plenty of precedence already exists.

If you wait long enough, anything will flow: Reiner has quoted the Prophetess Deborah, who said, "The mountains flow before the Lord." (The Hebrew verb is often wrongly translated "melt".) Some glasses and pitch are generally treated by rheologists as solids, though both will flow under the smallest loads if we wait long enough. Very slow deformations usually measured under either constant load or load per unit area (since the cross-section of a rod decreases as it lengthens) are known as *creep*. Creep has its greatest importance in metal rheology and will be discussed in Mr Graham's appendix. But plastics and other non-metals also show creep. Most rheologists agree to include within this term both eventually recoverable and also permanent deformations.

The apparent viscosity may either fall or rise with increasing shear-rate but the former is by far the more common behaviour. Many of the systems which show this effect are two-phase dispersions, either *suspensions* (solid

18

particles) or *emulsions* (liquid particles) in a liquid medium and we will consider their general properties in a later chapter. Some of these systems are liquids, i.e. they start to flow at the lowest measurable pressures; others have solid properties; a certain well-defined stress, called the *yield-value* must be reached before flow starts.

With regard to the former, Wo. Ostwald (son of the famous Wilhelm) long ago proposed that the flow processes consisted of a number of stages as shown in Fig. 4.1.

I. At the very lowest rates of shear, the flow would be Newtonian.

II. Very soon, however, the apparent viscosity would fall, generally varying as a constant power in the shear-rate. (These power equations will be discussed later.) Since this was supposed to be due to a breakdown in structure, this phenomenon was called "Strukturviskosität", generally translated as *structural viscosity*. The term has been criticized on the grounds that the names of phenomena should not depend on theories of their causes. At a well-defined shear-rate, all the structure should have been destroyed and this is followed by a region of Newtonian flow rather misleadingly called the *laminarast* or *laminar branch* of the curve. "Linear branch" would have been better.

Finally, flow ceases to be both linear and laminar and small eddies are set up around the rotating particles due to local turbulence. This region is

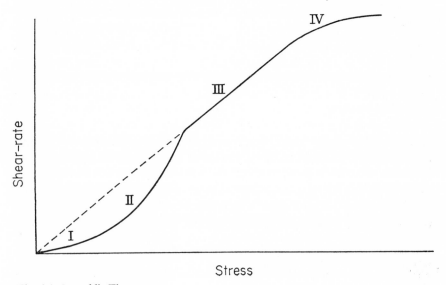

Fig. 4.1 Ostwald's Flow-curve

described as called "Strukturturbulenz". It was many years before there was much conclusive evidence for the existence of these four regions, but this has accumulated with time and the general scheme seems to be correct for many systems. Simplifying slightly a nomenclature proposed by Burgers and Scott Blair (1949) "structural viscosity" is now generally known as *shear-thinning*.

In some cases, Stage II only is found within the experimental range studied. The term *pseudo-plastic* was at one time used to describe this.

It is less easy to picture a mechanism which would cause an increase in apparent viscosity with increasing shear-rate. There would seem to be two distinct possibilities. In 1885, Osborne Reynolds,* in developing a most peculiar theory for the structure of the Universe, pointed out that close-packed spheres, such as particles of sand, before they can be sheared, must move into open packing. The system dilates, i.e. increases in volume, and flow tends to become increasingly difficult. This phenomenon is known as *dilatancy*. It is quite wrong, however, to use the term "dilatancy" to describe the behaviour of systems which are not known to "dilate", even though the system may not dilate as a whole, but rather in patches.

The increase in apparent viscosity may be due to quite other causes and again, the name of a phenomenon should not depend on unproved theories of its cause. A much better general term is *shear-thickening*; or if flow comes to a complete standstill, *shear-blocking*. Many textbooks and scientific papers show a figure illustrating an increase in apparent viscosity with rising shear-rate and labelled "dilatancy". This is bad nomenclature.

It is not difficult to propose other possible causes for shear-thickening: for example, the rising stress might well tend to push dispersed particles together and to cause them to form a structure; or the rising shear-rate might produce more frequent "collisions" or close approaches of particles to one another. It is certainly true that shear-thickening is much less common than shear-thinning.

Many paste-like materials show a yield-value, followed by a linear flow curve. (A "flow-curve" generally means a curve plotting shear-stress τ against shear-rate $\dot{\gamma}$).† The first to investigate these systems thoroughly was E. C. Bingham. Since he believed that fluidities were generally more useful properties than viscosities, he concentrated attention on what he called the *mobility*, i.e. the (constant) rate of shear divided by the stress minus the yield-value (or more exactly the extrapolated intercept of the straight line onto the stress

---

* Reiner, in his "Deformation, Strain and Flow", has pointed out that Osborne Reynolds was not the first to describe dilatancy.
† The usual symbol for amount of shear is γ. "Newton's dot", as it is called, indicates the rate of change of this with time.

axis). The reciprocal of the mobility is generally known as the *plastic viscosity*. It has, of course, the dimensions of a viscosity. Such systems are known as *Bingham systems*. Some materials show a yield-value followed by either shear-thinning or thickening. There would seem to be no general name for such systems. Anomalies of flow in capillaries will be discussed in the next chapter.

The presence of a yield-value indicated a kind of static friction: a force which must be overcome before any flow can take place; and we see that we now have three basic types of behaviour: Hookean, which may be represented by a coiled spring; Newtonian, represented by a piston operating in a cylinder of a Newtonian liquid such as an oil (since these are often used to damp machinery under the name of *dashpots*, this term is generally used for this model) and a weight resting on a flat surface, called a *slider*. This is also known as a *Saint-Venant system*.

Many materials behave as if they were built up of combinations of these three elements in series and in parallel and early rheologists often used to try to design quite complex models of this kind to describe the behaviour of their materials. It even used to be thought that the elements of these models represented specific physical components of the system; but this can rarely be the case. The models really represent a series of exponential equations and may just as well be replaced by electrical analogues, such as resistances and capacities. "Model making" is not as popular as it used to be but there are still occasions when it is helpful, especially to those who do not think easily in terms of even quite simple equations.

It has been pointed out that quite often, apparently different models really represent the same mode of behaviour. Roscoe (1950) was perhaps the first to point out that all such models of dashpots and springs (he does not discuss sliders) may be classified as belonging to two "canonic types"; (a) units of a spring and a dashpot in parallel linked in series, together with a single spring and a single dashpot and (b) units of a spring and a dashpot in series all linked in parallel. Of course any one of these units, notably the single dashpot in (a), may be missing, or have such a high viscosity that it can be ignored (see Fig. 4.2).

In earlier times, Reiner was prominent in classifying many of these models and naming them after their inventors. This was valuable work at the time but I do not think that the rheologist of today need memorize them all.

The two simplest models of all, however, must be considered in detail. The first, a dashpot and spring in series, represents the simplest process of *relaxation* of stress, first studied by J. C. Maxwell in 1868. If such a model is quickly stretched to some preselected strain and held at that strain, because of the flow in the dashpot, the stress must be continuously reduced. The rate

c

at which the dashpot will flow will, at any moment, be proportional to the force, i.e. to the extension of the spring so that this force will fall exponentially, i.e. a graph plotting the logarithm of the force against time will give a straight line. From this line, one can find the time taken for the force to fall to $1/e^{th}$ of its initial value, if we use natural logarithms on the base e. This is known as the *relaxation time*. Maxwell himself knew well that many systems do not behave in this simple way, and his equation is therefore the "basic equation" for relaxation. Some systems are represented by more than one dashpot and spring in series and have more than one relaxation time: still more complex systems show a continuous range ("spectrum") of relaxation times and the equations for their distributions may be worked out. A very common distribution is that of Wiechert in which the distribution follows a normal probability law ("Gaussian distribution") if plotted on a logarithmic time scale. (This is not as difficult to test as it sounds. If the ratio of the stress at time t to the initial stress is plotted on special probability–logarithmic graph paper, which is easily obtained, it can be shown that, if a straight line results, the Wiechert distribution holds quite closely—see Scott Blair and Burnett 1959.)

"Maxwell systems" are non-Newtonian liquids, or *elastico-viscous* and whether they will seem to behave like elastic bodies or like liquids will depend on the ratio of the relaxation time to the time of duration of the experiment. Thus, if a spring and dashpot in series is extended and then immediately released, the dashpot will not have time to flow, and the system will behave elastically. If, on the other hand, it is held extended for a long time, the dashpot will flow and reduce the tension on the spring, so that the system

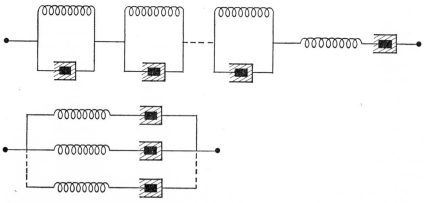

Fig. 4.2 Canonic types of Dashpot-spring Models

will behave almost like a Newtonian liquid. The relationship between relaxation time and experimental time is thus highly important and has been called by Reiner the *Deborah number*, following the quotation already cited.

Although a minimum of mathematics is included in this book, the very simple equations for the two principal models which describe the elastico-viscous and visco-elastic behaviour will be given. The equation for a Maxwell system in the form applicable to shear, is: $\dot{\gamma} = \dot{\tau}/G + \tau/\eta$, in which G is the shear modulus and the other symbols have already been defined.

Visco-elastic behaviour (also called *anelasticity*) is so called because it implies an ultimate complete recovery after the stress is removed. It is represented by a spring and a dashpot in parallel. When a constant stress is applied, the spring will stretch gradually at a rate which depends on the rate of flow in the dashpot and this will itself depend on the extension of the spring. This means that there is a critical "time", analogous to the relaxation time, which may be defined, under load as that required to reach a fraction $1 - (1/e)$ of the strain to recover. This time is now always known as the *retardation time*, though in older papers, the term *orientation time* was sometimes used. The slow building up of an elastic strain is generally called *elastic fore-effect*. Slow recovery is called *elastic after-effect*. This model used to be called after Voigt but it seems that priority should really be ascribed to Lord Kelvin. The equation for the Kelvin model is: $\tau = G\gamma + \eta\dot{\gamma}$. Although this system is a solid, we see that it contains a damping viscous element and the viscosity of this dashpot is sometimes called the *solid viscosity*. It was at one time called *firmo-viscosity*.

Many systems combine elastico-viscous and visco-elastic behaviour (indeed some rheologists do not think it worth while to distinguish the two terms, but this is confusing). The simplest combined model is ascribed to J. M. Burgers and is shown in Fig. 4.3.

This is a very fundamental model and many real materials approximate to it. It has a relaxation time (η_1/G_1) and a retardation time (η_2/G_2) and the ratio of these, which I have called the *springiness number* (a dimensionless

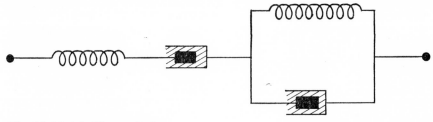

Fig. 4.3 Model of Burgers System

ratio), is a fair measure of the "springiness" or what is confusingly but popularly called the "elasticity" of a material (Scott Blair 1958). "Springiness", as subjectively assessed, depends on the extent of elastic recovery when a material is squeezed and then released and also on the speed of this recovery. The former is measured by the relaxation time (or more correctly the "Deborah number") and the latter on the *reciprocal* of the retardation time, since a large retardation time implies slow recovery. More complex systems will, of course, have more than one "springiness number" but the principal one may often prove to be of practical importance. Since the flow of the Maxwell dashpot in the Burgers model is irreversible, Burgers systems are, of course, liquids.

The only other model we will show here is the Bingham model (Fig. 4.4).

Slider

Fig. 4.4 Model of Bingham System

Systems which will withstand small stresses, such as the force of gravity, but which flow at higher stresses are "mouldable", since they can readily be given some desired shape which they will not lose when left standing. This property is called *plasticity* and many attempts have been made to define it in quantitative terms. Some of this work will be discussed in the next chapter. In the mean time, we will close with a quotation from Brongniart, written in 1884 but still true today, referring to plasticity: "on a souvent parlé de cette propriété, on semble la connaître, mais on n'en a qu'une vague idée."

5/Flow of Complex Systems through Capillaries

By the term "capillary", in this chapter, we shall mean a long narrow cylindrical glass tube of even bore. When we come to discuss the flow of blood in a later chapter, we shall find that the term is also used in a different sense by haemorheologists.

Let us return for a moment to the Poiseuille-Hagen law for a Newtonian fluid. We will do an "imaginary" experiment in which a capillary is filled with a liquid (or two liquids having the same viscosity) half the column being coloured and the other half colourless. We will suppose that, at the start of the experiment, there is a sharp boundary as shown in Fig. 5.1 and marked A.

After a given time, following the application of a pressure (say 1 second), the boundary will be curved, as shown. It is assumed, and it is true in the majority of cases, that the liquid in contact with the wall does not move. The "particles"* of liquid flow in lines parallel to the wall. The rate of motion of each particle of liquid *relative to the wall* increases progressively to the centre but the rate *relative to its neighbours* is greatest at the wall and becomes zero at the centre. This latter rate is given by the slope of the curve, a vertical line of particles (as at B) would indicate zero slope. The mathematics of this will be found in Appendix 2. Suffice it here to say that the curve shown is a parabola, but we have shown it only in cross-section: in reality it is a solid figure, a paraboloid and it is in general known as the *figure of extrusion*. The rate of motion of a particle relative to its neighbours is known as the *velocity*

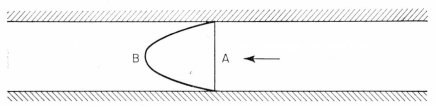

Fig. 5.1 Figure of Extrusion of a Liquid in a Capillary

---

* One could usually say "molecule" rather than "particle" but the argument here is entirely general.

25

gradient and, in this special case, is equivalent to the rate of shear. The rate of shear is therefore maximal at the wall and zero at the centre of the tube; and since the viscosity, defined as the shear stress divided by the rate of shear, is constant, the same must be true of the stress.

Here we see at once a disadvantage in the use of capillary viscometers for non-Newtonian systems, i.e. that the rate of shear and the stress are not constant across the tube. The flow described above is *streamline*. If the liquid is flowing fast or the density is high and the viscosity low, eddies will be formed and the Poiseuille-Hagen law will not hold, the flow being *turbulent*. The onset of turbulence depends on the value of a dimensionless ratio called the *Reynolds' number* (Re). This is given, in a capillary, by twice the volume flow per second multiplied by the density and divided by π times the radius times the viscosity. The exact value of Re will depend on the geometry of the apparatus, e.g. the smoothness of the ends of the capillary. In general, turbulence is supposed to start when Re exceeds a value of about 2000.

All this is by way of introduction so that we may consider what happens when systems which do not obey the Poiseuille-Hagen law flow through capillaries.

Much of the earlier work was done on systems like clay pastes which follow approximately the Bingham model. Consider what happens when such a paste is caused to flow through a capillary at a series of increasing pressures. The

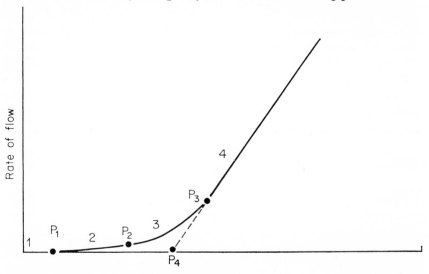

Fig. 5.2 Flow-curve of a Paste Flowing through a Capillary

"flow-curve" will consist of four fairly well-defined parts, as shown in Fig. 5.2.

(1) Up to a certain well-defined pressure (P_1) there will be no measurable flow at all. (2) When P_1 is reached the static friction at the wall of the capillary is overcome and the clay flows as a solid plug along the capillary, somewhat like toothpaste coming out of a tube. The rate of flow will be proportional to $P - P_1$ where P is the (increasing) pressure. (3) When P reaches the value P_2, which represents the yield-value when the stress is highest at the wall, streamline flow will start at the wall. As pressure is still further increased, the streamline region will increase in width towards the centre, leaving a "plug" of diminishing size at the centre, and the flow curve will bend upwards. (4) Finally, the yield-stress will have been exceeded virtually through the whole tube and the flow curve will again be a straight line. This line may, of course, be extrapolated to an intercept on the pressure (or stress) axis (P_4) which is sometimes regarded as a kind of second yield-value, since it occurs in the very simple equation for the Bingham model.

Not all pastes show measurable plug flow and, in early times, Bingham noticed that his experiment curves "tailed off" into the region we have numbered "3". In 1921, E. Buckingham, in the U.S.A., found the true explanation and calculated that the experimental yield-value should have a value (ignoring plug flow) of 3/4 P_4. In 1926, M. Reiner, in Palestine, tackled the same problem not knowing of Buckingham's work and derived the same equation (except that he did not allow for plug flow). This equation is therefore known as the "Buckingham-Reiner equation".

In practice, many pastes do not behave quite as simply as this and a ratio for P_3/P_4 is found to differ significantly from 3/4. R. K. Schofield and I published many papers on this in the early thirties. I believe we were the first to introduce the initial static friction term corresponding to P_1.*

When I was in America (1929-30) I found an unexplained relationship between values of the constants for the plug flow of ceramic clays and their plasticity as assessed by experts. This seemed to me to provide a possibly useful way of measuring "plasticity" but, so far as I know, the method has never been used. The reference is given in case anyone should care to pursue the matter (Scott Blair 1931). (A very full account of this work is given in my first book: "Introduction to Industrial Rheology", 1938.)

There is another important respect in which many pastes and suspensions fail to obey the Poiseuille-Hagen law: in this case it is the fourth power of the radius term that is invalid.

---

* I did some of this work before Schofield joined our team with B.A. (now Sir Bernard) Keen and with E. M. Crowther.

The earliest record of this would seem to be in a paper by E. C. Bingham and H. Green in 1919, who noted that certain paints have higher mobilities in very narrow than in somewhat wider tubes; but these authors did not follow up this finding. In 1930, Schofield and I (Schofield and Scott Blair, 1930) found a similar type of behaviour for thick pastes of soils (removing only the coarse sand and still larger particles) and for clays prepared from soils. In a series of four papers (of which only the first is listed here) we made a very thorough study of the phenomenon. A method of plotting the data from a number of capillaries was used which would have given a straight line passing through the origin if the fourth-power law had held. In fact the line was fairly straight, but made (on extrapolation) an intercept on one of the axes. We wanted a symbol to represent the slope of this line and, since at that time "S" was almost always used for stress, we chose the Greek sigma (σ). The intercept, we called σ_0. The whole phenomenon came to be known as the *sigma phenomenon*. According to the suggestion of a later author this term related to a proposal made some ten years later by F. J. Dix and myself; that, in certain materials only (including soil pastes), the phenomenon might have been caused by many of the soil particles having been large by comparison with the radius of the capillary. The calculation of any formula of the Poiseuille type involves an integration, i.e. the assumption of infinitesimally thin layers of material shearing past one another. We suggested that, in the case of soil, a better model would be to suppose a series of layers of finite thickness and when Mr Dix worked out the corresponding equation using a summation instead of an integration, his equation fitted extremely well with the data which Schofield and I had published ten years previously for soils. The sign for a summation is a capital sigma (Σ) but this had nothing to do with the name of the phenomenon.

I have never believed that this "summation" theory explains all sigma phenomena. Many factors would seem to be responsible. In the case of soil and clay pastes, Schofield and I first thought that the flat, plate-like particles of clay, though somewhat aligned in flow in all parts of the tube, were more aligned by the proximity of the wall. But when we tested pastes of a number of different minerals, we found that those whose particles were more nearly spherical showed the phenomenon if anything more markedly than did the plate-like particles.

Our second idea was that, for reasons then unknown, there might be a reduction in concentration of particles near the wall. Using a metal tube with a small hole in the side, we determined the amount of clay in the extruded paste but could find no difference between this and the concentration of the bulk of the material.

Nevertheless, we now know that for some materials, such as blood, this dilution at the wall certainly plays a part in the sigma phenomenon. Poiseuille himself (and even earlier workers) had noticed a layer near the wall of the blood vessel in which there were few corpuscles, now known as the "plasmatic zone", which will be referred to in a later chapter.

In 1931, Fåhraeus and Lindquist (1931), in Sweden, quite unknown to Schofield and myself, had independently discovered the sigma effect in flowing blood. It was many years before we came to know of one another's work.

During the past thirty years, sigma phenomena have been found in a great number of systems and have been much studied, especially recently, as we shall see later, in the case of blood.

There are many possible causes. It is known that elongated particles and also deformable particles will tend to migrate away from the wall of a capillary. The classical papers on this are those of Jeffery (1922) and Taylor (1932).*

V. Vand and, in rather a different way, R. L. Whitmore, have pointed out that, in the case of a model of a suspension of spheres, the free space between the spheres can be smaller in the bulk of the suspension than it is close to the wall, where it is obvious that the centre of a particle must lie at least as far from the wall as the length of the particle radius. Isaac Newton is said to have observed the change in trajectory of a tennis ball when it is "cut", and Bernoulli worked out that, when a particle rotates, so that one "side" of the particle is moving faster than the opposite "side", there will be a force tending to move the particle sideways. Even spherical particles moving in a capillary will tend to rotate, by reason of the viscous couple (i.e. the difference of stress on the two sides). But it is doubtful whether this effect, known as the *Magnus effect*, could be large enough to account for sigma phenomena.

With very small capillaries, the sigma phenomenon is often quite large. It has been suggested that, because of the similarity of its mathematical expression to that of plug flow, it is just a form of the latter. But, at least in the pastes studied by Schofield and myself, the two phenomena were quite distinct, the sigma effects being several hundreds of times as great as the effect of plug flow.

Many experiments have recently been done on model systems of very small spheres suspended in liquids of the same density. At first, the results appeared to be not only very complex but even contradictory. Now it is apparent that they depend on the Reynolds' numbers at which the experiments are done. Thus, from Israel, Segrè and Silberberg (1961) reported that, not only did particles fairly near the wall migrate away from it but also particles at the

---

* Taylor did not suggest that the particles would move radially.

centre tended to move away from the centre, towards the wall, producing what they called (by analogy with quite a different well-known phenomenon in physics) a "pinch effect".

Goldsmith and Mason (1961, 1962), in Canada, have published a number of papers on these phenomena. In their earlier experiments, it appeared that rigid spheres do not move sideways in capillary flow; but later, working at much higher Reynolds' numbers, they confirmed the existence of a pinch-effect. The cause of the outward movement, away from the centre, would appear still to be somewhat obscure.

It has also been suggested that sigma effects are due to a very rapid type of thixotropy (see next chapter), i.e. a breakdown of the structure of the system which recovers rapidly but not immediately, when the stress is removed. It seems unlikely, however, that if such a mechanism exists it would not also produce anomalies for different lengths of tube. Shearing through a tube twice as long should surely increase the alleged breakdown. This is not found to be the case for pastes which show the sigma phenomena, though P. Zamboni has shown that there is a "length anomaly" for certain mucins.

I have given here a rather sketchy account of the very large amount of work that has been done on sigma phenomena, avoiding (as always in this book) all the difficult mathematics. A rather more complete history of the subject was given by me at the 3rd International Congress on Rheology (Scott Blair 1958b) but much has been published since then.

An important aspect of this question is whether complex materials always wet the walls of capillaries, i.e. is there really no flow at the wall. M. Reiner studied this question as early as 1932 and developed a formula essentially the same as that of Schofield and myself. The question of "slip" has recently again been raised in relation to blood flow, which will be discussed in a later chapter.

6/Hysteresis and Rheotropic Effects: Normal Forces

So far, we have considered mainly "monotonic" systems, for which there is one definite stress associated with each value of the shear-rate. Exceptions are Kelvin systems and dilatancy.

Consider a Kelvin system attached in series to a dashpot as shown in Fig. 6.1.

If this model is extended very slowly, that is, in relation to the viscosity of dashpot *a* it will show flow like a liquid. But if pulled out fast, or if the viscosity at *a* is high, if strain is plotted against a series of increasing loads, followed by a series of decreasing loads, a loop is formed, a permanent strain remaining at the end of the cycle. Many real materials behave somewhat like this but, if the cycles are repeated always in the same direction (say, pulls on a cylinder), the specimen hardens and the curves get steeper. If now at some point the direction of stress is reversed (compressions), the immediate effect is a dramatic softening, later followed again by hardening. This effect, though commonest with metals, has been found with some plastics and even with renneted milk gel ("junket"). It is known as the *Bauschinger Effect* and is shown diagrammatically in Fig. 6.2.

This is a type of *hysteresis*. By a strange coincidence this word, derived

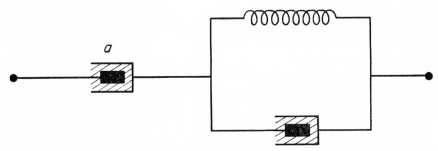

Fig. 6.1 Model of Kelvin System and Dashpot in Series

31

from the Greek, really does mean that the behaviour of a system at any moment depends on its previous history.

A somewhat similar effect is to be found with a certain type of dilatancy. If a rod of certain clays (e.g. plasticine) is held, one end in each hand, and gently pulled and released a number of times it will be felt to soften—until a certain clearly defined extension is reached. If an attempt is made to stretch it beyond this point, it hardens so much that it will generally rupture. This phenomenon has been called *backlash*.

It is clear that there is a big difference between this and the behaviour of a Kelvin body. The former is irreversible unless the whole mass of clay is re-moulded and does not depend on a "Deborah number". The Kelvin body, on the contrary, can be made to show a perfectly reproducible stress–strain relation if the time of the experiment is large compared with the retardation time. (The Deborah number was defined in terms of the relaxation time. It is not, in fact, incorrect to call the ratio of viscosity to elastic modulus of a Kelvin body a "relaxation time" but it is convenient to make a distinction and use the term "retardation time".)

The term *rheotropy* is used in the title of this chapter. Proposed by P. G. H. Boswell in 1951 (I believe), it has been little used by rheologists; but I introduce it here because it is a very useful term. It includes a number of pheno-

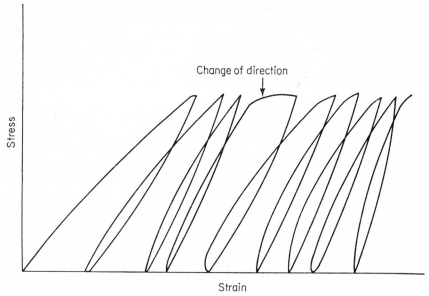

Fig. 6.2 Hysteresis and Bauschinger Effect

mena which we shall now discuss about whose nomenclature there is still controversy among rheologists. We will approach this question from a historical angle.*

It must have been known for a long time, in certain industries, that some materials become runnier when stirred and tend to re-set on standing. I do not know when the term *false-body* was first applied to this phenomenon. I believe that T. Péterfi, a pupil of Herbert Freundlich, was the first to introduce the term *thixotropy* in 1927: certainly Freundlich and his school were the first to make a thorough study of the phenomenon. The original definition (quoted from Boswell) was slightly unfortunate: "the isothermal reversible gel/sol/gel transformation of a colloidal system, produced by mechanical disturbances such as shaking, and subsequent rest." This would seem to imply that in the undisturbed state, the system must be a solid gel and in the stirred condition, a liquid sol. In fact, very few real materials show this extreme type of behaviour. I spoke to Professor Freundlich about this shortly before his death and he assured me that he had no objection to extending the definition to include any loss of consistency on stirring with a measurably slow recovery on resting but definitely *not* to include systems whose recovery is so rapid (in relation to the experimental time) that the stress appears to be a monotonic function of shear-rate ("shear-thinning"). Since he invented the term "thixotropy", I think it best to keep to this ruling.

Before considering the relationship between thixotropy and false-body, we must deal with the term *rheopexy*. Confusion in the use of this term is most unfortunate. It was first invented by Freundlich's pupils, Juliusburger and Pirquet (1936). Their definition is perfectly clear: "the solidification of thixotropic sols by gentle and regular movement." Thixotropic sols will, of course, solidify in time without this "movement"; but, with some substances, the re-setting is accelerated by gently rotating the beaker containing the material. This is the phenomenon as described by Juliusburger and Pirquet. For some twenty-five years this term was always used in the literature in the above sense; then, most unfortunately, it began to be used for systems, not necessarily in the ordinary sense thixotropic, sometimes apparently to mean shear-thickening and sometimes, I believe, to mean *anti- or negative-thixotropy*, a rare phenomenon in which a "thin" material thickens when stirred and loses consistency when left to rest. This phenomenon was, I think, first described by Eliassaf, Silberberg and Katchalsky (1955).

To return to rheopexy, there is now extreme confusion in the literature. In papers published before about 1960, the term has the meaning given to it

---

* A very good review article on this subject is that of Bauer and Collins (1967).

by its inventors: since then, it has come to be used for quite other phenomena. Is it too late, I wonder, to try to rectify this confusion by going back to the original definition?

The distinction, if any, between thixotropy and false-body is a more difficult one. Most rheologists use the terms synonymously; or rather tended to say "thixotropy" in the laboratory and "false-body" in the factory, at least until the so-called "thixotropic paints" became known to the public.

Yet it would be wrong to dismiss out of hand the views of a very able rheologist, the late Mr J. Pryce-Jones, who did many careful experiments in this field; Pryce-Jones always maintained that there are two quite distinct phenomena. It is worth quoting him verbatim: "In a 'false-bodied' paint, therefore, there is a very rapid increase in viscosity, which soon reaches a maximum value corresponding to the low solid concentration in the system under discussion. In the 'thixotropic' paint there is a very slow initial increase in viscosity, but the increase continues for a long period of time and ultimately reaches a very high value corresponding to the high solid concentration." Using a coaxial cylinder viscometer, Pryce-Jones found quite different shapes of deflection-time curves for these two systems. These phenomena naturally have great importance in the paint industry, since the paint should have a low consistency when brushed but should very quickly harden after the coating has been laid.

Drilling muds should be "runny" while the drill is operating but should set firm when at rest. Heather honey (from Ling, not bell-heather) is prized for the large air bubbles which remain suspended in it because of its rigidity but must become spreadable when stirred with a spoon or a knife. In view of all the confusion of terminology, Boswell's term "rheotropy" would seem useful to include all of them.

What are the causes of rheotropy? It was at one time thought that these phenomena occurred only when needle- or plate-like particles formed together into a structure which could easily be destroyed by shearing. The attractive forces responsible for the structure would re-establish it after the shearing was stopped. Rheopexy would be produced by the gentle rotation's helping this re-forming process. It is now known, however, that there are cases where almost spherical particles show rheotropy. Nevertheless, the same sort of mechanism is probably responsible.

Some materials soften when they are sheared but do not recover their consistency (or at least not fully) when left to set, even for long periods. This phenomenon used to be called *Rheodestruction* (from the German "Rheodestruktion"), but etymologists do not like words to be derived from a mixture of Latin and Greek and the term is, in any case, clumsy. After consulting a classicist friend, Reiner and I have dared to propose a new term, derived entirely from Greek: *rheomalaxis*. It remains to be seen whether other rheologists will approve.

We have already mentioned systems which harden when they are strained. These phenomena will be discussed in Mr Graham's appendix on rheology of metals, for which they are most important. The term *work-hardening* should, strictly, refer only to a rise in yield-value when a material is strained but is often used to include any increase in consistency.

Hysteresis phenomena of all kinds are difficult to measure in numerical terms. Various attempts have been made, over the years, to define an "index of thixotropy", starting with C. F. Goodeve and G. W. Whitfield in 1938 (the slope of the curve plotting the viscosity against the reciprocal of the shear-rate). This applies rather to shear-thinning than to what we should now call thixotropy and it has been pointed out that what it really describes is a kind of yield-value. Much later, H. Green, in a posthumous book, also proposed an index of thixotropy. This is all very well for certain special thixotropic systems tested in exactly the same arbitrary way in a particular viscometer. (Both Goodeve and Green used coaxial cylinders.) Long ago, I myself proposed a "number" for thixotropy of heather honey but I was under no delusions that it was any more than a useful figure obtainable only if a quite arbitrary procedure was carefully followed. In fact, I poured the honey into a measuring cylinder, left it standing overnight and, the following morning, measured the time of fall of a standard ball-bearing through a known height. I then stirred the honey in a carefully standardized way, with a stirrer consisting of a hold plate attached to a metal rod and timed another falling ball. The ratio of the times of fall before and after stirring gave me a useful measure of thixotropy; but my figures would have been quite different had I used a different method. The reason is that thixotropic phenomena (amount and rate of breakdown and of recovery) depend on stress, strain and rate of strain. Any equation explaining thixotropy independently of the method of measurement would have to contain many parameters. This is not to say that an empirical "index" of some kind may not be very useful for practical purposes.

Another rather interesting property which, as we shall see later, has practical applications in human and veterinary medicine, is commonly called *flow-elasticity*. This term should really refer to the behaviour of elastic liquids in general (as described in the next chapter) but in fact is generally used for behaviour in a capillary tube when certain mucous materials (and also some of the not very high molecular weight polymers) are extruded from a capillary tube, so as to form a "blob" at the exit, and the pressure is then sharply released, the mucus will recoil along the tube, sometimes all the way back to where it started. Such materials can usually also be drawn out into long elastic threads. Any highly viscous liquid can be drawn into threads, but the length of the thread is proportional to the viscosity of the liquid. These exceptional substances, however, are not usually very viscous. The phenomenon has, so far, almost always been called by its German name, *Spinnbarkeit*, but Reiner and I have invented an English equivalent, *Spinability*. (We decided, after some discussion, on one "n".) Spinability and flow-elasticity usually go together—but there are some materials that show one phenomenon and not the other.

What is actually happening? This is probably really a type of hardening (*strain-hardening*, not technically work-hardening). When a thread is drawn out, it is never perfectly even in diameter or strength and normally, where it thins, the force per unit area increases. The local situation gets worse and worse and the thread breaks. This phenomenon is called *Striction*. But with a strain-hardening material, the very fact of the increased strain at the weak (or narrow) point causes a hardening, so that the thread keeps its cylindrical shape; and very perfect cylindrical threads are indeed formed. If the material happens to have high-elasticity, these threads will retract when broken and much the same mechanism is probably responsible for flow-elasticity, the material gripping tightly to the wall of the capillary.

We are here dealing with elastic forces acting in the opposite direction to the force originally applied. Sometimes a force acting in one direction, or in one plane, will produce a force at right-angles. Such forces are known as *normal forces*. A well-known case is the so-called *Weissenberg Effect*. We do not know who first noticed that, if a rod (or the inner cylinder of a coaxial viscometer) is rotated in certain materials, although all the forces are in a plane parallel to the ground, the material will climb up the rod, against the force of gravity.

The first written record of this would seem to be in a doctorate thesis written by R. J. Russell, but its appearance was delayed for security reasons during the Second World War. (It was finally published in 1946.) Soon after the war, a number of workers, notably Pryce-Jones, Reiner, Rivlin and Weissenberg, worked, both theoretically and practically, on this phenomenon. It is generally conceded that Professor K. Weissenberg played the biggest part, and the phenomenon is now always known as the *Weissenberg effect*.

It is easy to explain this by saying that there is an extra finite component in the stress tensor but, as already stated, this is no "explanation". What really happens is still a matter of controversy. Two very simple (perhaps over-simple) analogies may help. The first is what is known as "strangulation". If you squeeze a cylinder of deformable material around its circumference, it will elongate. The second idea postulates very long chain molecules. If you start winding a string round a rotating rod, it will, of course, wind "up" the rod. These are, of course, very crude pictures. The complete mechanism (if indeed it is always the same in all systems) is still a matter of acute controversy and is not suitable for discussion in an elementary book of this kind.

Long before the presence of these normal forces was appreciated, R. K. Schofield and I noticed that, when we made cylinders of flour-doughs by pushing the dough out of a kind of grease-gun, the "strong" flours (i.e. those that would make a good big loaf) gave cylinders which swelled sideways and had a rough surface; whereas the "weak" doughs gave very smooth cylinders, hardly bigger in diameter than the tube out of which they were forced to extrude. Unfortunately we did not record this in our published papers, although we tried (unsuccessfully) to make a test for strength from measurements of the diameter. This sideways swelling is now well known in the plastics industry and is generally called the *Barus effect*.

Finally, nearly forty years after publishing his classic paper on capillary flow, Professor Reiner* has described some strange phenomena when two disks are set very close together and parallel to a high degree of precision. If one disk is rotated, air will be pushed out by centrifugal force, but if the disks are exceedingly close together, air is drawn inwards. This constitutes a kind of "centripetal pump". This effect might be found as an artifact if the plates were not perfectly parallel; but only, I understand, for gases. The same effect is found by Reiner using a liquid (toluene). But the interpretation is still at a highly controversial stage. The *Poynting effect* in metals (see Appendix 1) is somewhat similar.

Note. In this chapter, we have had occasion several times to use the term "consistency". Fortunately, attempts to give this term a connotative definition have failed. It is much needed as a general term and was well defined long ago by the (American) Society of Rheology as "that property of a material by which it resists permanent change of shape and is defined by the complete flow-force relation". Its meaning is generally understood by the man in the street.

---

* Many articles: but see especially Reiner (1963).

7/Elastic Fluids. Sinusoidal Straining. "Intermediacy"

We have already said something about elastic liquids. A Maxwell system is an elastic liquid with a single relaxation time and materials that show flow-elasticity in a capillary tube are usually much more complex elastic-liquids.

In recent years a method new to rheology, partly borrowed from the electricians, has become increasingly popular for studying elastic liquids. It is especially suitable for systems which, through some physical or chemical process, gradually change from being preponderantly liquid to being mainly solid in their behaviour, such as renneted milk or certain starch suspensions. The method also has the advantage that, with modern electronic recording, it may be used with such small strains that the system is not appreciably altered by the straining. We will consider here this method only in its simplest form; but at some length, since in most textbooks and articles in which it is described, the reader is assumed to be familiar with the parallel phenomena in electricity.

Qualitatively, the principle is to put the material to be tested into a hollow cylinder which is caused to oscillate alternately clockwise and anticlockwise, through a small angle. Within the sample is hung a solid cylinder attached to a torsion wire. The presence of the material will cause the inner cylinder also

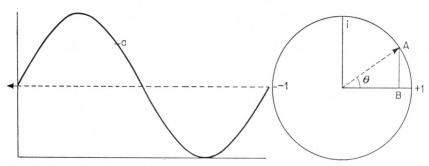

Fig. 7.1 Sinusoidal Curve

to oscillate and the torque on the wire may be measured by the movement of a spot of light on a scale, reflected from a mirror attached to the wire, or by much more sophisticated methods.

The relation between the enforced oscillations of the outer cylinder and the response of the inner cylinder becomes very simple provided that a particular type of oscillation is applied. This is called *sinusoidal* and is explained as follows.

Imagine a clock-face, with a single hand rotating in an anticlockwise direction. The hand is of unit length and has a pen attached to the free end. If there is a paper behind the clock-face on which the pen writes, a circle will be drawn. But suppose that there is a strip of paper which is itself drawn sideways at a convenient constant speed. The pen will now trace a wave-like graph as shown in Fig. 7.1.

When the pen has moved from the horizontal position to the point A, the graph will have reached the point *a* on the paper. The distance above the base-line is marked AB; and since the "hand" is of unit length, this is equal to sin θ, where θ is the angle through which the arm has turned. The curve so plotted is therefore that of t $\propto$ sin θ, where t is time, and is therefore called "sinusoidal". The outer cylinder of our viscometer is made to follow a curve of this shape. More complex curves can be analysed by what is known as a Fourier analysis which adds further terms to the very simple equation for the sinusoidal straining; but these terms do not appear, even for curves of more complex form, provided that the curves do not change appreciably when the frequency of oscillation (ω) is changed.

Consider what happens when a perfectly elastic system is tested in this way. This type of oscillation implies that the torque (or stress) is highest at the top and bottom of the wave-curve, i.e. when the cylinder is changing direction and is momentarily stationary; whereas the rate of shear is highest in the middle of the swing when the stress is zero.

For an elastic body, the modulus, stress ÷ strain, is constant, so that the maximum of the stress curve will be found at the time of maximum strain and, if we draw a wave-curve to represent the applied strain and a second curve for the measured stress, these curves will be "in phase", i.e. the maxima and minima will occur at the same times. The vertical axes, representing stress and strain, will, of course, have different scales, since the dimensions differ. The amount of twist of the outer cylinder is not an immediate measure of strain, which depends on the angle between the outer and inner cylinders, but this is easily calculated.

If we have a Newtonian (high viscosity) liquid between the cylinders, the torque on the inner cylinder will depend on the viscosity, i.e. the stress ÷ the *rate* of shear, which is at its maximum when the strain is zero. This means that the maximum of the stress curve will correspond to the minimum of the strain curve—i.e. the curves will be exactly "out of phase". This is shown in Fig. 7.2. The angle between these curves varies from 0° for the elastic system to 90° for the viscous liquid. For elastic liquids, it will come somewhere between the two. This means that, in the course of each swing, a part of the energy is stored elastically and recovered on the counter-swing and a part is lost as heat and is not recovered. The "real" elastic modulus is, of course, a function of the former; and the viscosity, of the latter. But how can we express a total or "*complex modulus*" as it is called, as a sum of these two parts, since viscosity and modulus have different dimensions?

The usual way, borrowed from the electricians, is to describe the viscous part in terms of what is rather quaintly called "the imaginary part of the modulus". This comes about in the following way: If you return to Fig. 7.1 you will see that I have marked the "3 o'clock and 9 o'clock" points on the dial as "+1" and "−1" respectively. This is the usual convention. So, if we want to change the sign, we must rotate the arm through two right-angles; in fact "−1" means "rotate through two right-angles". The "numbers", such as −1, or it might be 2, 3, 4 etc., are really *operators*. "+2" means "move twice as far to the right"; "−3" means "move three times as far to the left".

But how can we describe the points at the top and bottom of the curve? We must find some operation which, when done twice, will change the sign

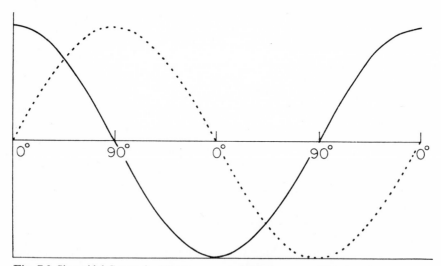

Fig. 7.2 Sinusoidal Curves for Viscous------ and Elastic ——— Systems

without changing the magnitude. If we represent this operation by the letter
"i",† then $i \times i = -1$ or $i = \sqrt{-1}$. Since there is no real number which
is the square root of minus one, "i" is generally called an "imaginary number". W. W. Sawyer, in the best elementary account that I know of all this
and which has inspired the present explanation ("Mathematician's Delight",
Pelican) points out that there is really nothing "imaginary" if we consider i,
not as a number, but, as explained above, as an operator: i.e. "turn the axis
through 90°". (I have found differences of opinion among mathematicians as
to whether it is correct to call i a number.) It might be wondered why these
operators are not additive, i.e. $+2$ would mean "move two places to the
right" and -3 "move three places to the left". This would still mean that a
change from $+1$ to -1 would signify a rotation of 180° but, for the movement through two individual right-angles, we should then have $2i = -1$ or
$i = -1/2$. There already is a point on the horizontal axis corresponding to
$-1/2$, so that this would offer no explanation for the introduction of a
second dimension at right angles.

Now we can write an equation for the complex modulus, which is always
written G*, as the sum of a "real" part of the modulus G' and an "imaginary"
part iG'': $G^* = G' + iG''$.

It is clear that the ratio of the real to the imaginary parts should depend
on the angle by which the two curves are out of phase ("the phase angle" v).
How can we express v in such a way that G''/G' becomes infinite (i.e. no
elasticity) when $v = 90°$ and becomes zero, when $v = 0°$ (i.e. no viscosity)?
A glance at our tables will show that the tangent of v will do just this, so we
have: $G''/G' = \tan v$. But it must surely be possible to describe G'' as a
viscosity. The real elastic modulus is represented by the stress divided by the
amplitude. The viscosity would be represented by the stress divided by the
rate of shear, which depends on the amplitude multiplied by the frequency.
In what follows, we are no longer concerned with direction, and viscosities
and elastic moduli are, of course, scalar quantities, so we need not introduce i.
The theory of dimensions will be discussed in a later chapter. Here it is
sufficient to point out that a stress is a force per unit area and must have
dimensions mass $\times$ acceleration $\div$ area or $ML^{-1}T^{-2}$; a strain, being an
angle, has no dimensions, so that an elastic modulus will have the dimensions
$ML^{-1}T^{-2}$. A rate of strain is a number per second and must have dimensions
T^{-1}, likewise a frequency. Viscosity must therefore have dimensions $ML^{-1}T^{-1}$.
To express the imaginary part of a modulus as a viscosity, it is thus necessary
to divide it by a quantity having dimensions T^{-1} and the relevant property

† In branches of physics other than rheology, the letter "j" is now more often used but
rheologists generally keep to "i".

of the sinusoidal curve, is therefore, the frequency. Thus we can write $G'' = \eta''\omega$. In fact the whole equation may be re-written in terms of viscosities: $\eta^* = \eta' + i\eta''$. To distinguish such viscosities from those obtained under steady† flow conditions, they are often known as *dynamic viscosities*: likewise *dynamic moduli*. In the case of viscosity, this is a trifle confusing, since in earlier times ordinary viscosities were sometimes called "dynamic" to distinguish them from "kinematic" viscosity, which we shall discuss later. (A slightly more advanced treatment of the method of sinusoidal straining is given in a paper by Marvin (1952).)

As has already been said, this method and more complicated modifications of it, enable materials to be tested over a wide range of frequency into such small strains that they are hardly changed by the process of testing—a general criterion for measuring a physical property. But there *is* a danger here. Rheology is a very practical science and we generally want to know how materials behave in the course of manufacture or use. These "dynamic" properties, though often valuable in elucidating the molecular structure of materials for example, are seldom directly related to practical conditions and it is usually "processes" rather than classical physical "properties" that interest us.

Many years ago I proposed an alternative way of getting over the difficulty of making direct comparisons between (in the extreme case) viscosities and elastic moduli. Though I did not realize it at the time, it has a certain similarity to the "imaginary number" device. Although it arose mainly from psychophysical experiments, which will be discussed in a later chapter, I shall briefly describe it here.

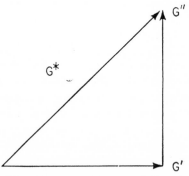

Fig. 7.3 Vector Diagram of Complex Modulus

---

† Much of the early work on steady flow was published in German and the word "stationär" was used. This was wrongly translated into English as "stationary flow"; which, as Reiner has pointed out, makes nonsense! The best translation is "steady".

We have seen how to calculate the *proportion* of the energy which is stored elastically for an elastic liquid under sinusoidal straining but we have not considered how to find the actual values of G′ and G″ in the equation. Elastic moduli and viscosities are, of course, scalar quantities: nevertheless it is possible to draw a type of vector diagram as shown in Fig. 7.3. From Pythagoras' theorem we find $|G^*| = \sqrt{|G'|^2 + |G''|^2}$. (The vertical lines, which, for convenience are written in only once, mean that we are considering the magnitude only and not the "direction" of the modulus. It is thus possible to draw "vector diagrams", since we are dealing with numbers. G* is given as the ratio of the maximum stress to the maximum strain. Knowing the value of G″/G′, we can then calculate both G′ and G″.)

The diagram proposed by me was in some ways analogous. It depends on the following argument: a viscosity is defined as a shear stress (τ) divided by the rate of shear ($d\gamma/dt$). A shear modulus is given by τ/γ. The strain (γ) may be formally written as $d^0\gamma/dt^0$ and its first differential as $d^1\gamma/dt^1$. There is psycho-physical evidence that, in judging the firmness of materials by handling them, the real criterion is not a mixture of viscosity and elasticity but as intermediate entity which we may describe as $\tau \div d^\mu\gamma/dt^\mu$ where μ is a fractional number: normally $1 > \mu > 0$. Equations integrated from this fractional differential* were shown to fit compression and relaxation of many soft plastics during the Second World War.

If one had a series of elastic materials each with a different shear modulus, one could display these as points at different distances along a line—i.e. in a single dimension. Likewise, if one had a series of liquids of different viscosity,

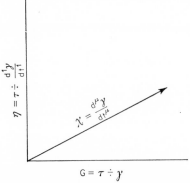

Fig. 7.4 Illustrating Principle of Inter-mediacy

---

* It seems that the use of the fractional differential has been independently proposed in 1966 by T. D. Shermergar in the U.S.S.R.

one could place these at intervals along a line at right-angles to the former line. Again, the magnitude of each viscosity is described by a single number.

Now suppose we have a substance whose behaviour lies intermediate between those of a solid and a liquid, we could draw a vector-type of diagram with a line lying between the vertical and horizontal axes of length corresponding to the magnitude of the "property" analogous to shear modulus and viscosity (see Fig. 7.4).

The sine of the angle ϕ is a measure of μ, i.e. of where the substance lies within a continuum whose dimensions vary regularly and progressively from $ML^{-1}T^{-2}$ on the horizontal axis to $ML^{-1}T^{-1}$ on the vertical axis.

This is really just another way of getting over the dimensional discrepancy between an elastic modulus and a viscosity. It does not involve the use of an "imaginary number" but it introduces the idea of a two dimensional continuum in which the behaviour of a material must be described by two inseparable quantities (μ and χ). Since some (but by no means all) physicists object to calling such entities "physical properties", I long ago proposed that they should be called "quasi-properties". Apart from a limited amount of work in the psycho-physical field, this idea has not been followed up; but I still feel that some rheologists, more skilled in mathematics than I am, might some day make good use of it.

8/Dispersed Systems. Effects of Concentration and of Electrically Charged Particles

When a solid or liquid is "dispersed", i.e. distributed as small particles, in a continuous liquid phase, we have a *dispersion*. If the particles are solid, this is called a suspension; or, at high concentrations, a paste. When the dispersed particles are liquid, it is called an emulsion (as defined in an earlier chapter).

There is no adjective "disperse" in the Oxford Dictionary. This, in itself, does not preclude us from inventing such an adjective for technical use but no good purpose seems to be served in leaving out the commonly accepted "d" and therefore, though many rheologists write "disperse system", I shall not do so.

The simplest question to start with is to ask what happens when a small number of homogeneous rigid spheres is added to a Newtonian liquid. Presumably there will be a rise in viscosity and eventually viscous anomalies will appear.

Again we have a "basic equation" and this was derived, in the most brilliant years of his career (1905–6), by Albert Einstein. This was within a year of the time at which, at the age of 27, he published the Special Theory of Relativity.

His equation, with one interesting exception which we shall discuss later. applies only to very dilute suspensions of non-interacting small rigid spheres, It is:* $\eta_{rel} = 1 + 2{\cdot}5\phi$, where η_{rel}, the *relative viscosity*, is the ratio of the viscosity of the suspension to that of the pure continuous phase and ϕ is the volume concentration. This may be written in an even simpler form. If we define a so-called *specific viscosity* (η_{sp}) as the relative increment in viscosity, i.e. $\eta_{rel} - 1$. So we have $\eta_{sp} = 2{\cdot}5\phi$.

You will notice that, although these two properties are called "viscosities", they do not have the dimensions $ML^{-1}T^{-1}$. They are ratios of viscosities, i.e. pure numbers. The adjective "relative" makes this quite clear but the term "specific" is quite arbitrary and would be misleading if it were not so well known.

---

* The factor 2·5 did not appear in Einstein's first calculation: it was added later.

Before going on to consider how this basic equation has been modified to allow for higher concentrations and non-spherical and electrically charged particles we must quote the one remarkably exceptional case in which Einstein's equation holds for a most unlikely material; at least if we generalize the constant 2·5 to have other values. Arnstein and Reiner (1945) showed that cement mortars of concentrations up to 60% sand in cement obey this law. This is possible because the very high concentration is offset by the extremely high viscosity ($\sim 10^{17} - 10^{18}$ poise).

We shall not deal with all the proposed modifications of Einstein's equation—there are over fifty of them!* In discussing the most important equations, we shall follow a logical rather than a historical order, though Hatschek's equation happens to come first either way.

In 1912, E. Hatschek proposed an equation to allow for concentrated suspensions at high enough rates of shear to eliminate viscous anomalies:

$$\eta_{\text{rel}} = \frac{1}{1 - \sqrt[3]{\phi K}}$$

where K was called the *voluminosity factor*.

"Voluminosity" implies that some of the continuous phase is attached to the dispersed particles, thus increasing their volume. Some of the Dutch rheologists later proposed a number of complex modifications of Hatschek's equation.

Two other lines of thought have been developed. First, the Arrhenius equation: $\ln \eta$ is linear with C, which is the concentration as weight per unit volume (most of the later equations express concentration in this way and not as volume/volume). This equation holds well for many systems if they are freed from electrolytes; but by far the most widely used modification of the Einstein equation was, I believe, first proposed by Guth in about 1936, though it is difficult to be sure of the priority.

The idea is very simple. We generalize Einstein's 2·5 to a number A which differs for different systems and we expand his equation into a series: $\eta_{\text{sp}} = AC + BC^2 + \ldots$, again using C in place of ϕ. In fact the first two terms are often sufficient and, dividing both sides by C, we have $\eta_{\text{sp}}/C = A + BC$. η_{sp}/C is called the *reduced viscosity*. Graphs of reduced viscosity against C will often be straight lines for low concentrations and may be extrapolated† back to zero concentration to give a value of A which was, over many years, called the *intrinsic viscosity* and written $[\eta]$. This name has been criticized on the grounds that the term "intrinsic" is meaningless in this

---

* An excellent general summary is given by Rutgers (1962).

† This must be an extrapolation because when $C = 0$, η_{sp} will also be zero.

context and that the property is not a viscosity. Alas it is not even a pure number, since C is generally given in grams per decilitre. But the alternative terms proposed seem no better: the following table gives three of the principal proposals in the English language.

Table of viscosity-concentration nomenclatures

Symbol	$\eta_\sigma : \eta_{rel}$	$\eta_{sp} = \eta_{rel} - 1$	$\eta_c : \eta_{sp}/C$	$[\eta] : \left[\dfrac{\eta_{sp}}{C}\right]_{C \to 0}$
Original term as given above	Relative viscosity	Specific viscosity	Reduced viscosity	Intrinsic viscosity
U.S. National Research	Solution-solvent viscosity ratio: viscosity ratio	Viscosity ratio increment	Staudinger's differential Viscosity concn. index: Viscondex	Limiting viscondex
International Joint Committee on Rheology (1949)	Viscosity ratio	Viscosity ratio increment	Staudinger's viscosity number	Kraemer viscosity number

In spite of these later proposals—the others—the nomenclature given above is still the most widely used.

The intrinsic viscosity, by whatever name it is known, has a very wide importance. It is essentially a generalization of Einstein's constant 2·5 and it can be shown that it is given as well by the slope of the Arrhenius plot as by the more usual intercept of the extrapolated reduced viscosity plot. Staudinger (who called it, in German, "Viskositätszahl") believed it to be proportional to the molecular weight of the dispersed material. It is now generally accepted as proportional to a power of the molecular weight, not necessarily unity. (Probably first proposed by H. Mark or Staudinger himself.) Unfortunately, the concept of "molecular weight" for solutions of polymers is very complex and there are various statistical "averages" which are determined by different physical measurements. This subject is outside the scope of our book: suffice it to say that the type of average measured by intrinsic viscosity is a somewhat unusual one.

With shear-thinning systems the intrinsic viscosity is seldom affected directly (at zero concentration) but the linearity of the curve may well be.

In such cases, the reduced viscosities are generally taken from an extrapolation of the $\eta/\dot{\gamma}$ curve to zero shear-rate or to very high shear rates at which viscosity will be effectively constant.

Many modifications of the above treatments have been proposed and I have found it difficult to select, out of the vast literature, those items which would seem essential in an elementary study.

As with viscosity itself, so with intrinsic viscosity, there are rheologists who prefer to work with reciprocals—notably Ford (1960). He redefines most of the properties that we have discussed in reciprocal form and claims that this gives better straight lines, partly on data from reconstituted milk. D. R. Oliver and S. G. Ward have proposed somewhat similar equations.

The reader may come across the term *inherent viscosity*. Here there is some confusion, because at least one author (R. H. Wagner) has proposed this, with the symbol $\{\eta\}$ for the value of the reduced viscosity at an arbitrarily selected finite concentration; but the term is more generally used to designate the logarithm of the relative viscosity divided by the weight concentration, in the Arrhenius plot.

Considerable work has been done on suspensions in which the spherical particles are not all of the same size. Roscoe (1952) proposed two equations; the first for particles of uniform size at rather high concentrations: $\eta_{rel} = (1 - 1\cdot35\phi)^{-2\cdot5}$ and the second, for particles of very diverse sizes: $\eta_{rel} = (1 - \phi)^{-2\cdot5}$. At very low concentrations, all these equations reduce, of course, to $\eta_{rel} = 1$; but at rather low concentrations $\ln(1 - \phi) \simeq -\phi$ and we get the Einstein equation.

It is not my intention, in this book, to say much about the rheology of emulsions. My friend Dr P. Sherman will shortly be publishing a companion volume which will deal fully with this subject. One fundamental paper must, however, be mentioned.

Taylor (1932) proposed a rather complex equation, which need not be given here, to allow for currents set up within the liquid drops; but in many cases it has been shown that small drops behave more like solids and Taylor's corrections may be neglected.

Two more effects must be considered: first, what is known as the "self-crowding factor". When the concentration of a suspension is increased, there is not only an increase in the volume of the dispersed phase but also a relative decrease in that of the continuous phase. In a series of papers, V. Vand has proposed a correction for this and has also claimed to develop some theoretical justification for the Arrhenius plot, but M. Mooney has criticized part of Vand's theory. Vand's equation is $\eta_{rel} = k\phi(1 - Q\phi)$ and is similar to that of Mooney. Q is known as the *self-crowding factor*. Working on sodium caseinate derived from milk, J. C. Oosthuizen and I found that Arrhenius' equation held so long as the system was almost completely free of electrolytes. As sodium chloride was gradually added, the graphs showed increasing curvature. This could be corrected by introducing an arbitrary series of values of Q. But these values turned out not to be as "arbitrary" as we had supposed, since they gave a linear plot against intrinsic viscosity. Unfortunately the work had to be discontinued at this point.

The last effect to be discussed in this chapter is that of electric charges which are generally present on the dispersed particles. By far the best account of the history of this rather complex subject is given by Conway and Dobry-Duclaux (1960).

The story starts with M. von Smoluchowski in 1916, who proposed a complicated modification of the Einstein equation to allow for charges on the particles. It is now known that there are three principal ways in which such charges can increase the intrinsic viscosity of a dispersion. These phenomena are known as *electro-viscous effects* and we will abbreviate this, for convenience, to "e.v.e." The effect considered by von Smoluchowski is now known as "primary e.v.e." and does not generally play any very large part in increasing viscosity. It is limited to the rather unusual conditions that the particles are insulating, rigid, without swelling, insoluble, stable, very small and spherical, and that they are sufficiently far apart for there to be no electrical interaction between them. "Secondary e.v.e." is due to the overlapping and interaction of the layers of ions around the particles. Suppose that the particles bear negative charges, then there will tend to be an accumulation of positive charges around each particle; and for some distance away from it, there will be at least a statistical tendency for positive and negative charges to alternate. This "electrical overcoat" is known as the "Gouy layer".

It is often stated that secondary e.v.e., produced by the interaction of this "atmosphere" of ions, can occur only in non-Newtonian systems but I believe that this is not correct.

The third type of e.v.e. is produced by a stretching out or uncoiling of long-chain molecules due to the repulsion of like charges along the various parts of the molecule. This tends to occur when there are no free ions present to "screen" the charges and accounts for the fact that the addition of an electrolyte often reduces the viscosity of a suspension. It is frequently not easy to distinguish between the effects of secondary and tertiary e.v.e.

9/Theory of Dimensions: Power Equations: Turbulence

You will remember that, in Chapter 4, we said that the shear-thinning section of the Ostwald curve often followed a power relation between stress (τ) and shear-rate ($\dot{\gamma}$). We also agreed not to be too particular in distinguishing between "equations" and "laws". This power relation is, of course, not really a scientific "law"; nevertheless the term "power-law" is generally used.

We may write the equation $\psi = \tau/\dot{\gamma}^a$ or $\ln \psi = \ln \tau - {}_a\ln \dot{\gamma}$*. This means that we get a straight line if we plot either $\log \dot{\gamma}$ against $\log \tau$ or $\log \psi$ against $\log \dot{\gamma}$.

At about the same time as Ostwald published his ideas (around 1925–6) de Waele, in England, also proposed a rather more complicated form of power-law and was much criticized for so doing. Looking back over the years, one can see that there were justifiable criticisms but that not always the right ones were made.

The most general criticism, still often made of power-laws, is that they are "dimensionally inhomogeneous". This is incorrect, as we shall see in a moment. But de Waele did lay himself open to criticism on two grounds: first, he used the symbol η for something which does not have the dimensions of a viscosity, which is, to say the least of it, confusing; and secondly (much more serious) he introduced a term (using our symbols) $e^{-PR/2L}$. In the introductory chapter, we said that, in mathematics, nothing is forbidden that is not contradictory to logic; but this surely is illogical! When we write a power, such as x^b, we mean x multiplied by itself b times. Of course b need not be a whole number and it may be negative, since $x^{-b} = 1/x^b$. But b must be a number so long as we use this definition.† We cannot multiply e, or anything

---

* We generally use the abbreviation "ln" for natural logarithms which arise from all theoretical considerations and "log" for logarithms on base 10 which we actually use. I have used the symbol ψ in the log–log equation because the more usual η' is best reserved for the "apparent viscosity" which generally has the dimensions of a true viscosity.
† It would not be illogical to *define* $e^{|\tau|}$ as e multiplied by itself $|\tau|$ times, where $|\tau|$ is the numerical value of the stress in dynes/cm². This is not so very different from what we do in multiplication. 3×4 means 3 added together 4 times; but a mass of 3 g $\times$ a velocity

else, "a stress times"; it just does not make sense. de Waele might correctly have written $e^{-APR/2L}$, in which case A would have had the necessary dimensions to make the whole exponent into a number; but he did not do this.

Before going any further into the history of power laws in rheology, let us take a very elementary look at the Theory of Dimensions. It is obvious that we can divide a distance [L]* by a time [T] and get something quite different: a "speed" (L/T) if we want to know the speed at a given moment of time, we write dL/dT and if we make this into a vector, i.e. specify that it is a speed in a particular direction (say due north) we call it a velocity. Likewise we can multiply a mass by a velocity and get a momentum MLT^{-1}. It is usual (but not essential) to describe all physical quantities in terms of powers of mass [M], length [L], and time [T] and, except for electrical quantities which include $\frac{1}{2}$'s, these powers are usually small whole numbers. But we sometimes include other quantities such as temperature [θ]. Now it is clear that it is meaningless to add or subtract quantities having different dimensions; for instance we cannot say "5 grams = 3 centimetres + 2 seconds". This means nothing. If we add 3 apples to 2 oranges, we can only use the figure "5" if we ignore the difference between apples and oranges and say "5 fruit".

We have already seen that a stress, such as PR/2L (see Appendix 2) has the dimensions $ML^{-1}T^{-2}$ and viscosity $ML^{-1}T^{-1}$. If de Waele had introduced A into his expression, as proposed above, and if A had the dimensions $M^{-1}LT^2$, then all the dimensions would have cancelled out, and his expression would have been meaningful. Likewise, if he had written (as I have done) ψ instead of η, making it clear that this is not a viscosity, his power equation would have been "dimensionally homogeneous", i.e. the powers of mass, length and time could have been the same on both sides of the equation.

Returning to our simpler equation, we have:

$$\psi = \tau/\dot{\gamma}^a = ML^{-1}T^{-2} \div T^{-a} = ML^{-1}T^{(a-2)}$$

and both sides of the equation (including ψ) have these dimensions. The objection to this type of equation, then, is not that it is inhomogeneous but that it is not really one equation at all, but a whole series of equations, since for all materials for which the values of "a" differ, ψ will have different dimensions, i.e. will be a different "property". This is one reason why power equations hold for so many systems. To say that $\eta = \tau/\dot{\gamma}$ for various values of $\dot{\gamma}$, is a very simple statement: viscosity is a constant independent of the

---

of 4 cm/sec gives a value of 12 for quite a different and very useful property: momentum. The value, of course, depends on our choice of grams, centimetres and seconds.

* We generally use square brackets to indicate dimensions; so that L is a particular length (in de Waele's case, the length of a capillary) whereas [L] means the dimension of length—any length. But for simplicity, we will leave the brackets out in what follows.

values of τ and $\dot{\gamma}$. But our power equation (except in special cases which will be considered later) really means no more than that a series of materials all obey the same *kind* of equation: for some materials (or perhaps only one!) the stress is proportional to the square-root (the half-power) of the shear-rate: for others to the cube root (the one-third power) or the ·256th power, or any other fractional power (for shear-thinning) between 0 and 1.

We have already mentioned, in Chapter 7, that some physicists at least do not like to call such entities as ψ "physical properties" but I have written at some length on this subject because it is a common error to describe power-equations as "inhomogeneous", provided that a constant of variable dimensions is included to ensure that the powers of mass, length and time are the same on both sides of the equation.

As long ago as 1888, C. Bach found that some elastic systems did not obey Hooke's law and that the strain was proportional to a fractional power of the stress. In this particular case, dimensional difficulties can be avoided by turning the equation round: the stress is proportional to a power of the strain and the strain has no dimensions, nor does any power of it have dimensions.

We will not list all the papers, even the most famous ones, in which it is shown that stress varies as a power of the shear-rate, but a brief discussion as to *why* this should be so common is not out of place. If you put this question to most rheologists, they will give an answer which is, no doubt, often correct. They will point out that, if you have a slight curvature in a graph of, say τ vs $\dot{\gamma}$ this curvature will be reduced, perhaps to vanishing point, by plotting double logarithms, in this way including (theoretically) an infinite number of possible powers of $\dot{\gamma}$. It is *not* true that all curves become straight when plotted "log–log". This is easily seen from very elementary algebra or by experiment.

The special importance of log–log curves for metals will be discussed by Mr Graham in Appendix 1. This, it will be found, is closely linked with reasons given in my own chapter on psycho-rheology.

There are probably several other possibilities: one of these I have proposed for certain simple liquid suspensions (Scott Blair 1967).* It is suggested that these shear-thinning suspensions must have a structure when undisturbed. When sheared, this structure is broken down to some degree even under the smallest stresses, but so quickly recovered when stress is removed that there is no observable hysteresis. Although each shear-rate therefore has its characteristic stress, the effects of the stress and of the shear-rate on the structure are distinctive. The stress tends to break the bonds between the particles and

---

* I am indebted to Dr E. W. Evans for helpful discussions on this question, but he is not responsible for the views here expressed.

the shear-rate determines the difficulty with which they will re-form. The number of bonds between any two particles will be proportional to the stress needed to break the linkage, and also to the rate of shear needed to prevent their re-forming and the number of bonds is inversely proportional to the number of particles linked together. In practice, of course, there will be a distribution of bond strengths but, as we shall see in a moment, the experimental fact of log–log linearity can be explained by ignoring this and making the simplest assumption only.

It has been pointed out to me that the argument as given in Scott Blair (1967) begs a number of questions, and I will therefore recapitulate the theory here in its simplest form. It is not, of course, suggested that real suspensions behave exactly like this: the equations are essentially "basic".

The number of junctions per unit volume (Δn) broken down by an increment of stress ($\Delta\tau$) is presumed proportional to the amount of structure, which diminishes as τ increases. This is measured by the number of particles linked to other particles and inversely related to the minimum number of links in a junction, which is itself proportional to the stress. Hence

$$\Delta n/\Delta\tau = A/\tau.$$

At any shear-rate $\dot{\gamma}$, there is an inverse relation between the number of linked particles and the number of links in the remaining weakest junction which can be prevented from immediately re-forming by the addition of an increment of shear-rate $\Delta\dot{\gamma}$. Hence it seems reasonable that the number of junctions prevented from re-forming by this increment of shear-rate is inversely proportional to the shear-rate, or

$$\frac{m\Delta n}{\Delta\dot{\gamma}} = \frac{B}{\dot{\gamma}}.$$

(We must include a constant m because we cannot assume that $\Delta\tau$ and $\Delta\dot{\gamma}$ will have the same effect on n.)

But the number of bonds is so large that we may substitute d's for Δ's and, combining the two equations, we get

$$\frac{d\tau}{d\dot{\gamma}} = \frac{B}{Am}\frac{\tau}{\dot{\gamma}}$$

which, on integration gives the power equation.

A parallel argument for systems in which the potential-distance curves have a very different shape can be applied to explain shear-thickening. The stress forces the particles together and, as shear-rate increases, more collisions will take place, and the process of structure formation increases at a diminishing rate.

E

The power-equation is not restricted to liquids. Herschel and Bulkley (1926) were the first to propose the subtracting of a yield-value (τ_0) before taking logarithms; or $\ln \eta^* = \ln (\tau - \tau_0) - a \ln \dot{\gamma}$. The above treatment holds just as well for such systems and my own view is that this is probably something very like the mechanism that produces the non-Newtonian behaviour of blood, to be discussed in a later chapter. But the equation is not easy to use unless one has data at very low shear-rates. One must first draw a curve of τ vs $\dot{\gamma}$ and then extrapolate this, which is not a straight line, to the τ-axis to determine τ_0 before plotting double logarithms.

So far, we have considered power relations only between stress and shear-rate but a more general equation was proposed by Nutting (1921) of the form (using modern symbols and applying to shear stresses) $\psi = \tau^\beta \gamma^{-1} t^k$ of which our earlier equation is the special case where k = 1.

Although I met the late Dr Nutting in Washington in 1929, I had never heard of this equation and, some ten years later, my colleague Dr Valda Coppen and I published a paper proposing a similar equation, but initially implicitly taking $\beta = 1$ and k-values between 0 and 1. Naturally, as soon as we discovered Nutting's work, we made full acknowledgement of his priority.

Under constant stress, many materials give good straight lines when log strain is plotted against long time. My colleagues and I published many papers on the Nutting equation some twenty-five years ago. Except in relation to their application to psycho-rheology, to be discussed later, and the connection with Mr Graham's work on metals (Appendix 1) this work need hardly concern the reader new to rheology. It was, of course, often pointed out to us that the equation presents dimensional difficulties and sometimes we were wrongly accused of inhomogeneity. The former, which is a valid criticism, could easily be met if there were specific stresses, strains and times characteristic of the materials so that we could express the experimental data as ratios of these. We shall see later that this is occasionally possible. With regard to the alleged inhomogeneity, this mis-statement is so often made that it is worth while to give the reference to a formal refutation of it by a leading authority on the Theory of Dimensions: Dingle (1949).

In the meantime, M. Reiner pointed out that the Nutting equation "does not have the form of a physical law because the time coordinate appears in it explicitly". He and I proposed a form of the equation in which this was not the case. Today, I doubt whether this was as important as we thought at the time because the Nutting equation is always (or almost always) applied to conditions under which the "properties" of the material are being changed by the testing. Tests are not repeatable on the same sample. In such cases it seems doubtful whether the equation is, in any case, "a physical law" in the sense in which it is required that time does not appear explicitly. The treatment involved (using our present symbols) expressing τ, γ and ψ always as ratios of their first differentials with respect to time (or, more correctly, the reciprocals of these). This gave an equation in which each term would have the dimensions T^{-1} and did not include time explicitly.

There are some systems whose consistency increases with time. One hesitates to use the phrase "time-thickening", because, by analogy with "shear-thickening", this might seem to suggest that time causes the thickening. Time cannot, of course, be the cause of anything. Changes happen in time but the causes of the thickening are chemical and subsequent physical processes.

Two such processes are the "retrogradation" ("an association of molecules of amylose by hydrogen bonds") of starch paste and the early stages of the coagulation of milk. Two French workers, Y. Nedonchelle and R. A. Schutz, recently showed that, if a starch paste is held at a rather low constant temperature, during the gradual thickening which takes place, the double logarithmic equation $\log \eta^* = \log \tau - a \log \dot{\gamma}$ holds at a series of times and that the starch paste, in thickening, changes both in η^* and in its deviation from Newtonian behaviour (fall in a). They found, also, that if the values of η^* were plotted over quite a long period of time, against those of "a", a straight line was obtained. The equation for this line is $\log n^* = \log \alpha - a \log \beta$ where $\log \alpha$ and $\log \beta$ represent the intercept and the slope respectively.

Combining these equations gives $\log \tau - \log \alpha = a (\log \dot{\gamma} - \log \beta)$ or $\tau/\alpha = (\dot{\gamma}/\beta)^a$. You will notice there is no dimensional constant between the bracket in this equation and this means that it can be homogeneous only if τ/α and $\dot{\gamma}/\beta$ are dimensionless, i.e. if α has the dimensions of a stress and β of a shear-rate. We may therefore replace α and β by a definite stress τ' and a definite shear-rate $\dot{\gamma}'$ and it also follows that when $\tau = \tau'$, $\dot{\gamma} = \dot{\gamma}'$, i.e. there is a unique point with the coordinates $\tau' : \dot{\gamma}'$ at which all the log–log curves will meet on extrapolation.

When I read this interesting paper, my first thought was that this point would probably represent the condition when all the structure was destroyed, i.e. the beginning of the "Laminarast". This idea could not be tested from Nedonchelle and Schutz's data so my friend Dr W. Tuszyński (from Warsaw) and I decided to try to repeat and extend the experiment, using renneted milk.

If rennet is added to milk at a low temperature, the enzymes act on the protein in the milk, but the milk cannot coagulate until the temperature is raised. After leaving the milk in the cold overnight, we had to find a temperature by trial and error (and this differs from one milk to another) at which the coagulation would proceed at such a rate that we should have about two hours in which to take a series of flow measurements with changing (falling) rates of shear in a capillary viscometer before the milk "gelled".

Through the technical skill of my colleague, we managed to do this and were able to repeat the experiment enough times to be sure that we were getting results which obeyed the equations of our French friends. Moreover, by taking very frequent photographs of a falling column of milk, we could follow the curves up well into the "Laminarast" region and there is no doubt that, in practice, this is reached at much lower rates of shear than $\dot{\gamma}'$, the value of $\dot{\gamma}$ at which all our extrapolated log–log curves meet; so my guess was wrong.

What is the significance of all this? As Nedonchelle and Schutz pointed out, it means that for systems which thicken in this way, the dimensional awkwardness of the double logarithmic equation disappears, since the equation $\tau/\tau' = (\dot{\gamma}/\dot{\gamma}')^a$ is dimensionless. This is no doubt, a rather special case but we suspect that the same equations may apply to other similar systems.

We have said that our double logarithmic equation is, in general, really an infinite series of equations but, if we choose a single (fractional) value of "a", although the dimensions will be fractional, we shall have a single equation. This has been done by N. Casson, who originally plotted the square-root of the stress against the square-root of the shear-rate for data from "filled" varnishes. Assuming that the particles of the filler line up into "rods" and making some quite reasonable but nevertheless arbitrary assumptions about their behaviour, Casson was able to explain his equation, which has since been widely used for many other materials, including chocolate. Moreover, I discovered, some years ago, that many flow-curves (my own and still more from other published data) for blood followed this equation very closely.

Somewhat similar to Reiner's criticism of the Nutting equation, is a criticism of that of Casson. In the latter case it is pointed out that, suppose for example that the equation is applied to flow through a horizontal capillary, if, by convention, stresses acting from left to right are called positive, then those from right to left must be negative. This involves us in the square-root of negative quantities.

There is, as we have already seen, no objection to this as such but we can hardly postulate a property (the *Casson viscosity* defined as the slope of the $\tau^{1/2} : \dot{\gamma}^{1/2}$ straight line) as being a "real" quantity when measured in one direction and an "imaginary" quantity when the direction is reversed.

To meet this criticism, Casson, in his later paper, has put vertical lines around his symbols for stress and strain. This means that he is considering only the scalar parts of these quantities (called their "moduli") irrespective of direction, and is perfectly justified. Here is a case where we must not allow mathematics to seem to dominate physics. There is no reason why a quantity should not have a "real" square-root when it happens to be plotted to the left, rather than to the right. I say "seem to" because there is no really valid mathematical objection here.

Moreover, as with the Nutting equation, Casson's equation is generally, if not always, applied to systems which change their "properties" (often due to a rearrangement of dispersed particles) as they are sheared and the experiment cannot be immediately repeated merely by reversing the direction of the applied stress.

In a later chapter, I shall explain why I believe that Casson's equation is not the basic equation for blood flow; nevertheless it provides the most useful and quick method for expressing blood flow-curves from a single capillary in terms of two parameters and is now very widely used.

One could, of course, take any power other than $\frac{1}{2}$ and, for my own experiments, it seemed to me at least at one time as if $\frac{1}{3}$ would work just as well but this view is not generally accepted. It may be that other powers will fit other systems.

In the early days of rheology, equations consisting of series of powers of stress or strain were popular. The powers were whole numbers greater than 1, so that the general equation would be written (in modern symbols) $\dot{\gamma} = \phi'_1\tau + \phi'_2\tau^2 + \phi'_3\tau^3 + \ldots$ where the ϕ's represent a series of "apparent fluidities". But the argument of "direction" appeared, on the grounds that alternate terms must be left out because apparent fluidities must not depend on the direction in which the stress is being applied. It seems to me that there was really no need to make this restriction. We can get over the "grammatical" difficulty by writing always $|\tau|$.

Before leaving our discussion on power equations, mention should be made of what is, historically, their first use in relating stress to shear-rate. This is in the case of turbulent flow, when "a" is greater than 1, normally about 2. As we have said before, until recently, turbulence did not interest rheologists as a rule, because it was almost always studied as a part of hydrodynamics for the flow of water without reference to rheological properties. Recently, however, more and more attention is being given to the fluid dynamics of various non-Newtonian sludges. The subject is a difficult one and hardly comes within the scope of this book.

One interesting line of work, however, should be mentioned. A. White has recently shown that the "drag" on spheres moving through water is increased by the addition of certain high-polymer solutions due to the suppression of turbulence at high Reynolds' numbers. This increases the size of the "wake" behind the sphere. At low Reynolds' numbers (laminar flow) the drag on the sphere is correspondingly reduced as a result of the smaller "wake". In some cases the reduction in drag disappears on ageing the system. At the highest concentrations of polymer the system is non-Newtonian and there are Weissenberg effects.

10/Surface Rheology and other Surface Phenomena

In this chapter, we are on the borderlines of rheology. The phenomena to be described first are certainly rheological. Surface active molecules of substances now often called *surfactants* consist, in general, of two parts: a water-soluble part and a water-insoluble part. They therefore tend to lie on a surface of water, with the water-soluble parts dipping downwards and the insoluble parts standing up out of the water. This tends to produce a mono-molecular layer on the surface (or at high concentrations, layers several molecules thick). These layers can be placed between parallel baffle-plates and one of the plates can be moved so as to compress or expand the film; or a disk hung on a torsion wire may be placed on the surface, the water and the film being rotated in a cylindrical vessel. In fact, many of the usual methods used to measure "three-dimensional" viscosity and its anomalies may be adapted for work on surface rheology. For example, measurements of the drag on a torsion pendulum have been much used.

The rheological "properties", such as *surface viscosity*, will all have one dimension of length more than those of the bulk properties; i.e. an L^{-1} is eliminated because we are concerned with forces per cm and not per cm^2. Thus surface viscosity has dimensions MT^{-1} and *surface elastic modulus* MT^{-2}.

The best recent survey of work on surface rheology is probably that of Criddle (1960). Much excellent experimental work has been done by M. Joly and described in a series of papers in "Biorheology", 1962–7. It is not generally possible to shear only the surface layer and allowance may have to be made for the flow of the bulk of the liquid.

The substances studied have been mainly long-chain aliphatic acids, various aqueous detergents and some proteins. The relationships between the surface-rheological properties and chemical constitution are extremely complex and will not be discussed here in detail. Some layers are elastic rather than viscous and complex moduli can be measured much in the same way as described in Chapter 7. Some systems also behave as "two dimensional gases". Relaxation times have been measured for some proteins. Little is known about their relaxation spectra but the relaxation times vary from a few seconds to some minutes.

Joly (1966) has calculated interaction energies between undeformable molecules and the apparent energies of deformation and of internal cohesion of deformable molecules from surface-viscosity data. His experiments were done on proteins and polypeptides.

Surface rheology has practical applications not only in giving us information about the structure of surfactant molecules but also in connection with the formation and stability of foams and with the effectiveness of lubricants. This brings us to the complex concept of *oiliness*, or, as the Americans sometimes call it, "lubricity". (This term has another meaning in England and is perhaps unfortunate: the French "lubricité" must *never* be used to mean "oiliness"! My French friends use "onctuosité".)

Oiliness is a complex "property" by no means always highly correlated with viscosity. It is associated with surface-viscosity and especially with the effects of pressure on the latter but no simple formula appears to have been found for it.

It is often not easy to distinguish the effects of surface viscosity, elasticity, etc., from those of surface tension. The latter is caused, of course, by the dissymmetry of the forces acting on molecules at a surface. Molecules within the bulk of the liquid are acted on by forces of attraction and repulsion which are, in general, balanced in all directions, whereas those on the surface are not. It is incorrect to describe surface tension as similar to the presence of an elastic skin on the surface; the surface layer of molecules is in no sense Hookean. With complex materials, the values of surface tensions often depend on the method of measurement. Differences of the interfacial tension will sometimes produce movements of liquid. This is known as the *Maragoni effect*.

Problems of adhesion and cohesion fall on the border-lines of rheology. Adhesion depends on the properties of two materials which are caused to adhere. Many modern adhesives are stronger than the materials they join and, when rupture occurs, it is the cohesion of the materials which are stuck together that fails. Often it is not easy to distinguish the two phenomena and, for this reason, my friend Prof. J. C. Claassens, when working on the adhesive properties of butter, used the general term *hesion*. (This is analogous to "sorption" for ab- and ad-sorption.) Claassens found that the forces needed to pull apart two parallel surfaces of various materials with a butter layer between them depended greatly on the nature of the surface. He made a list of solid materials given in descending order of these forces. However, if the butter was sheared by drawing the two parallel surfaces apart by means of a sideways tension, the order of materials was almost exactly reversed.

A very common test for adhesions is known as the *peeling test*. A tape treated with adhesive on one side is stuck to a solid surface and then detached by pulling backwards. It is evident that such tests will not give the same results as those got from normally applied loads.

Adhesion will depend also on the roughness or smoothness of the solid surface. Here is a case where a term has been used by different rheologists in two entirely different senses. Some who worked with rubber described the roughness of the surface as *rugosity*; but other rheologists, working on powders, used the same term to describe the extent to which the particle of a powder differed in shape from a sphere, i.e. the reciprocal of *sphericity*. Neither use is very common and Reiner and I have not included "rugosity" in our recently published list of rheological terms. The study of the flow of powders has been called *Micromeritics**, which is also the title of an excellent book by J. M. Dalla Valle. E. C. Bingham, often described as "the father of modern rheology", worked on the flow of sand through narrow tubes.

Another property, closely allied to adhesivity or "stickiness", is *tack*. This is important for many industrial materials, especially printing inks and greases. The traditional method of assessing tack is to take a small sample between the finger and thumb and, on drawing them apart, quite a large number of short threads of the material will be formed and broken, if it is "tacky". Various "tackmeters"—instruments which imitate this procedure— have been invented. The best quantitative definition that Reiner and I could get from an expert in this field is as follows: "the force required to part, at a particular speed, two surfaces, or two surfaces separated by material of a special thickness, behaving as a liquid after a short time of contact." But I am not sure how widely this definition (in terms of a force) will be accepted. We have already discussed Spinability in Chapter 6. This is unlikely to be confused with tack, since the former is characterized by the formation of long, cylindrical threads, whereas tacky materials produce short, somewhat shapeless "threads"—if indeed one can use the word "thread" properly to describe them.

In connection with adhesion, we referred briefly to the nature of the surface of solid materials. This leads to all kinds of problems concerning friction and wear which belong to the science of "tribology", which is hardly a branch of rheology. But something should be said about the property of *hardness*. This is essentially a surface property: Reiner and I define it as "the resistance of

---

* See also a Symposium published in *Rheol. Acta*, **4** (3), 1965.

the surface of a body to penetration". Hardness has been traditionally measured on what might be called "the hen-pecking principle" in terms of what is
known as "Mohs' scale". If we take a series of minerals and place them in
such an order that each mineral will scratch the sample on its right and be
scratched by the sample on its left, numbers can be given to represent the
hardness of a suitable range of materials. There was, for a long time, however,
no evidence that the intervals in such a scale were equal or even in any
meaningful way related to one another. It was rather like parading a line of
soldiers in order of height. However, Tabor (1956) found that in fact Mohs'
scale gives equal intervals when plotted against the logarithm of hardness
measured by indentation.

Many methods have been used for measuring hardness by indentation with
spheres, cones, etc. These are used chiefly for metals, plastics and rubbers.
A simple procedure is to measure the depth of the permanent indentation
made after a penetrating body has been applied to a surface with a standard
force for a defined time. The original method as devised by Brinell was to
take the ratio of the applied load to the area of contact of the recovered
indent. Later workers used the projected area or the volume. The variation of
the diameter of the indent with load was generally found to follow a power-
equation and D. Tabor came near to giving a theoretical reason for this. The
exponent of the power-equation is generally known as the *Meyer Coefficient*
and is a measure of hardening rather than hardness.

American workers (L. Boor *et al.*) have claimed that there are at least five
partly correlated properties involved in hardness: (1) amount of indentation
under load, (2) amount of indentation after release, (3) amount of immediate
"return" of the indentation, (4) changes in optical properties caused by
abrasion and (5) loss of weight by abrasion. "Hardness" presents a slight
difficulty in nomenclature. The term *firmness* is denotative, i.e. it is not defined
in precise units and generally represents the resistance that a body offers to
handling or other forms of compression. Unfortunately we have only one
term for the inverse of both hardness and firmness: "softness". The use of
this word is, therefore, somewhat ambiguous.

11/Biorheology.
Part 1: Haemorheology

I suspect that quite a high proportion of the readers of this book will be concerned with biological systems. Although from the earliest days of rheology, there were always some, such as Poiseuille, who approached the subject from a medical or biological background, in recent years biorheology has played an increasingly large part in rheology as a whole.

Experimentally, the subject divides itself into two quite distinct sections: *in vivo* experiments and *extra vivum* experiments.* As soon as a material is taken from a living organism, it is apt to change its rheological (and other) properties.

By far the largest amount of biorheological work has been done in blood and blood vessels (haemorheology, a name proposed by my friend Prof. A. L. Copley) so a separate chapter will be devoted to this. In the next chapter, a number of other biological systems will be discussed.

It is interesting that as early as 1938, V. Nesfield wrote a book on the importance of blood viscosity in relation to a number of diseases but little attention was paid to his work. In a few diseases, such as Raynaud's syndrome, it is all too obvious that the viscosity of the blood is abnormally high.

Much of the work on blood and its components involves quite advanced mathematics as well as a considerable knowledge of haematological terms and is, therefore, beyond the scope of this book. Only a brief survey of the general principles will be given here. I am hoping, in collaboration with Prof. A. L. Copley to write a much larger book on haemorheology before so very long.

Blood consists of a suspension of red cells (erythrocytes), platelets, and white cells (leucocytes) in a continuous medium. This medium, when the

---

* The latter are generally called *in vitro* but, especially in the case of blood, experiments cannot usually be carried out in untreated glass vessels. My early memories of a classical education are confirmed by a classicist friend that *ex vivo* would mean "coming out of life" and that *extra vivum* is more correct. "Extracorporeal" is also used but this is a clumsy word.

particles are centrifuged off, is called "plasma". One of the principal constituents of plasma is "fibrinogen", which, following a long and complex
series of enzyme reactions, is converted through "thrombin" into "fibrin",
which forms the main structure of a blood clot. The liquid phase which
can be removed from clotted blood, and which therefore does not contain
fibrinogen is called "serum".

Whole human blood at high rates of shear behaves as an almost Newtonian
fluid with a viscosity about five times that of water. Plasma has a viscosity
about twice that of water and that of serum is somewhat less.

As mentioned in Chapter 9, at lower shear-rates, Casson's plot of the
square-roots of stress and shear-rate gives excellent straight lines both for
human and for bovine blood.

The distinction is important because the erythrocytes of human, but not
of bovine blood, form what are called "rouleaux", rather like a pile of coins
that has slipped sideways. These rod-like structures might bear some resem-
blance to the structures in the fillers in Casson's varnishes so that his theory
might be to some extent applicable to blood were it not for the fact that the
equation holds just as well for cow's blood which does not form rouleaux.

The fact that the Casson equation fits so well must depend on there being
a yield-value for blood, at least in the sense of a finite intercept on the
$(stress)^{1/2}$ axis when the Casson straight line is extrapolated. If the line went
through the origin, the system would be Newtonian. In fact careful experiments at very low shear-rates have shown that there is almost certainly a true

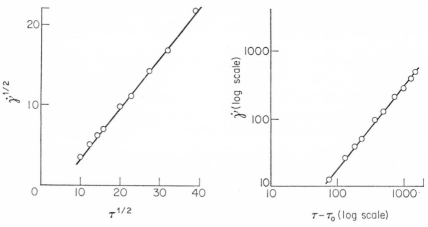

Fig. 11.1 A comparison of Herschel and Bulkley and Casson plots from Scott Blair's
published data on human blood (arbitrary units). (Reproduced with permission from: *Rheologica Acta*, Vol. 5, No. 3, pp. 184–187 (1966), Dr Dietrich Steinkopff Verlag, Darmstadt)

yield-value. Any attempt, therefore, to plot logarithms of stress and shear-rate directly is bound to fail to give a straight line. But, if the stress-strain curve is carefully extrapolated to the stress axis for data at low shear-rates, and the extrapolated intercept is subtracted from the stress before plotting on double logarithmic paper, the Herschel and Bulkley equation may be tested.

It is not possible for both this equation and that of Casson to hold over a wide range; but I have shown that, by taking theoretically perfect Casson data and plotting them converted to the Herschel and Bulkley equation, the deviations from linearity cannot be observed within one cycle* of stress, either visually, or by the usual statistical tests. Allowing for experimental error, this range must be extended to at least two cycles.

Although very many "Casson curves" for blood have been published, I have never found any which gave a single straight line over much more than this range. Figure 11.1 shows data for human blood plotted according to the two equations.

There is no doubt that, for practical purposes, the Casson equation is much easier to use but my own view is that it has, for the present at least, no theoretical significance as applied to blood. The Herschel and Bulkley equation, on the other hand, though subject to greater errors in practical use has probably some theoretical justification (see Chapter 9 and Scott Blair 1967) and I believe it to be the "basic equation" for the flow of blood through narrow tubes. (A. L. Copley points out that Poiseuille was himself the first to observe that the "basic equation" which he himself discovered does not hold for blood.)

It may be, perhaps, even before this book is published, that someone will find that, over many cycles, the Casson equation holds better than that of Herschel and Bulkley. If so, these conclusions will have to be revised; but some sort of theoretical explanation would also have to be found for the Casson equation as applied to blood, especially bovine blood.

It is generally assumed (see Appendix 2) that, when liquids flow through capillaries, there is no slip at the wall, though we know that with many pastes there is certainly "plug" flow (see Chapter 5).

We have already discussed a number of possible causes for the "sigma phenomena". In the case of blood, in which the principal dispersed particles (erythrocytes) are neither spherical (they are described as "bidiscoid") nor rigid, probably several factors play their part. I do not believe that my "summation" idea applies to blood: it was originally applied to thick soil

---

* The number of cycles refers to the characteristic of the logarithm: e.g. 1–10 or 10–100 is one cycle, 1–100 or 100–10,000 is two cycles, etc.

pastes. Certainly there is a drift of corpuscles away from the walls. Poiseuille, and even earlier workers, had observed a region called "the plasmatic zone" in which the corpuscles are few and far between.

Work at St Mary's Hospital, London, with radioactive indicators, has confirmed that the different corpuscles and the plasma flow at different speeds. A. L. Copley believes that the blood vessels are lined with a layer of fibrin-like material ("the endo-endothelial layer") whose homeostasis maintains the balance between a thickening and weakening of the vessel wall. It is claimed that these layers have been seen under the microscope but it is difficult to photograph them or to be sure that they are connected with fibrin. However, when he and I were working together we found (Copley *et al.* 1960) that, in glass tubes coated with fibrin, the apparent viscosity of blood (treated with heparin to prevent coagulation), was very considerably lower in fibrinized than in untreated tubes. It has been suggested that this was an artifact, produced by surface tension or by the hydrodynamic resistance in the wide tubes of our viscometer but I cannot see any justification for these criticisms. It is much more likely that it was caused by a slippage on the fibrinized surface of the tubes.

It seems that, in very fine capillaries, there is a negative sigma-effect: i.e. an apparent increase in viscosity as the diameter of the tube is diminished. This has been studied especially by L. Dintenfass. Some of this author's extensive work on blood rheology may be misunderstood if it is not appreciated that, unlike almost all other contemporary rheologists, he uses the term "thixotropy" to include shear-thinning. But A. L. Copley, L. E. Bayliss and others have shown that under certain conditions, blood is slightly thixotropic in the usual sense of the term: the apparent viscosity is higher in shorter than in longer tubes.

One of the most difficult fields of haemorheology is concerned with micro-circulation. How do the comparatively large erythrocytes squeeze through the tiny capillaries under what are known to be quite small pressures? The pioneer work in this field was done by Katchalsky *et al.* (1960) in a series of ingenious experiments in which erythrocytes were "haemolysed" (i.e. broken) by increasing the osmotic pressure around them both rapidly and slowly. The erythrocytes were found to behave like Kelvin systems (see Chapters 4 and 6), in that, when treated slowly, they would deform greatly and so presumably pass through tubes no wider than themselves; whereas sudden pressures would break them.

We have spoken of the treatment of blood with heparin to prevent its coagulation by glass. There are considerable differences of opinion as to how much such anticoagulates affect the apparent viscosity of blood and it is generally safer to line all glass vessels with silicone, which has a minimum of coagulating effect, rather than to add anticoagulants. Glass is a particularly active coagulant; but all materials, except the walls of blood vessels in people who do not have thromboses, will coagulate blood to some extent. This fact underlies Copley's theory of the endo-endothelial layer.

Other complications are that blood vessels are not cylindrical but conical (though the effect of this is probably not great); that flow in many vessels is "pulsatile", following the beating of the heart; and that it is not only (as used to be thought) in the largest vessels that there is turbulence. This last phenomenon brings us into the field of haemodynamics.

We have mentioned the long chain of reactions which ends in the formation of fibrin from fibrinogen. The fibrin molecules then link up together (polymerize) into a clot and it is interesting that the structure of this clot, as observed in an electron microscope, is quite different in the case of thrombi formed *in vivo* from what it is normally when the clotting is done in extracted blood. Nevertheless, it has been shown that a gentle shearing of the blood

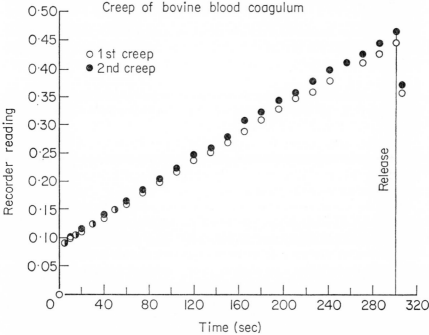

Fig. 11.2 Creep curve for Bovine Blood. (Reproduced with permission from: *Flow Properties of Blood and Other Biological Systems* (A. L. Copley and G. Stainsby, eds.) Pergamon Press, 1960)

during *extra vivum* clotting will produce a structure similar to that formed *in vivo*, when, of course, the blood is not stationary.

If I now describe certain experiments of my own on blood coagulated in siliconed glass tubes, it is not that I think that they are in any way superior to all the many other researches described in the literature, but because they are perhaps the simplest that can be done.*

Cow's blood containing a coagulant was put into a siliconed U-tube, the surfaces were covered with a little kerosene to prevent contact with air and, during the course of the coagulation, small air pressures were applied to one side of the column, the displacements on the other side being magnified and measured (Scott Blair and Burnett 1960). After a time, the clot no longer changed its properties very rapidly and it was then possible to do simple creep and relaxation tests.

For the creep test, a constant pressure was applied to the sample during 5 minutes. There was an immediate elastic reaction followed by a steady linear flow. When the pressure was removed, the elastic part of the deformation immediately recovered, i.e. the clot behaved as a Maxwell system (see Fig. 11.2).

In order to measure relaxation times, a long rubber tube was passed through a small mangle so that the air-pressure on the sample could be progressively changed by squeezing the tube. A pressure was applied so as to produce a convenient immediate displacement at the other end of the column. One experimenter maintained this constant strain by steadily reducing the pressure, while the other experimenter recorded the pressures at a series of times.

For a Maxwell system, the logarithm of the pressure as a fraction of the initial pressure should be linear with time. It will be seen from Fig. 11.3 that this is the case, except in the early stages of coagulation (only 17 minutes after the addition of the coagulants).

From the creep curves a viscosity and elastic modulus could be calculated and their ratio should be equal to the relaxation time. The viscous and elastic components were approximately Newtonian and Hookean respectively. It was, of course, not possible to do the two experiments simultaneously but alternative experiments were done as quickly as possible on the same sample and it was found that, except in the earlier stages of coagulation, the directly measured and the calculated values for the relaxation time agreed well. There was a progressive fall in relaxation time with age of sample. (For a full description of these experiments see Scott Blair 1960).

* My experiments on blood were made possible thanks to grants from the (U.S.) National Institutes of Health and from the British Heart Foundation.

In later experiments (Scott Blair and Burnett 1968), the dynamic properties of coagulating blood were measured. Two instruments were used: one was home-made. A cylinder attached to a spring was suspended in a cylindrical container into which was placed the coagulating blood. The second instrument (the thrombelastograph) was invented by my friend Prof. Hartert and is used by haematologists in many countries for measuring the coagulation and subsequent softening of blood clots (see Hartert 1952, and Hartert and Schaeder 1962). Prof. Hartert very kindly arranged for us to be lent one of these instruments. These two instruments work on much the same principle, though in the latter the pot is caused to oscillate and in the former, it is the inner cylinder that oscillates. In neither case is the oscillation strictly sinusoidal but it seems that the complex modulus of coagulating blood varies hardly at all over quite a wide range of frequency, so this does not matter.

Unlike our instrument, the thrombelastograph records the complex modulus on photographic paper so that charts are available for subsequent

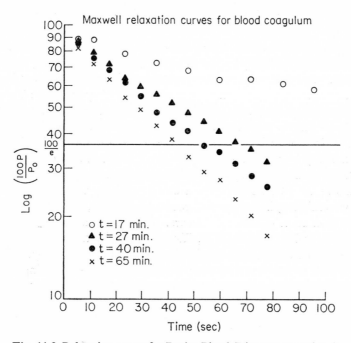

Fig. 11.3 Relaxation curves for Bovine Blood (P is pressure and P_0 is initial pressure). (Reproduced with permission from: *Flow Properties of Blood and Other Biological Systems* (A. L. Copley and G. Stainsby, eds.), p. 179, Pergamon Press, 1960)

F

analysis. These charts may be used for diagnostic purposes. We did not determine the dynamic modulus and dynamic viscosity separately but we found very simple equations relating the complex modulus (G*) to time, both in coagulation and subsequent softening. The diagnostic value of the "thrombelastograms" should be greater now that the equations of the curves are known, even if not fully understood. For further information the original paper should be consulted.

In the body, it is important not only that blood should coagulate in an open wound but that the clot should eventually be dissolved. This later process is called "fibrinolysis". A series of enzyme reactions, less well known but perhaps as complex as those involved in coagulation, finally results in the decomposition of the fibrin. It is not always easy to distinguish this process from one and possibly two others. As time goes on, the fibrin gel-structure drains away from the walls of the containing vessel, probably due to a type of orientation or "crystallization" within the gel. This is known as "clot retraction". Some workers believe that the phenomenon of "syneresis", common to most colloidal gels, in which liquid is pushed out from the fibrin gel structure, differs from clot retraction but much rheological and other work remains to be done before these phenomena are fully understood.

Fibrinolysis is normally produced by the action of an enzyme, plasmin, on the fibrin. In normal subjects, the phenomenon is not marked, but in certain diseases, such as prostate cancer and some liver disorders and also in cases of sudden violent death, the softening may be very marked and rapid. Substances are known which will encourage or inhibit both fibrinolysis and retraction in human blood. In our work already quoted* (Scott Blair and Burnett 1968) we showed that cow's blood does not always react to these substances in the same way as does human blood.

Cow's blood differs from human blood not only in this respect and (as already mentioned) in not forming rouleaux, but also, if left to stand, hardly any sedimentation of red cells occurs. Many years ago, the distinguished veteran haemorheologist, Prof. R. Fåhraeus† noticed that sedimentation was more rapid in blood from pregnant, than in that from non-pregnant women. It was at first thought that this might give a useful way of detecting pregnancy until it was found that there were also differences in Erythrocyte Sedimentation Rate (ESR) in men! Further study showed that, apart from pregnancy, an abnormally high ESR was associated with a number of pathological

---

* In one case, that of streptokinase, this was already known.
† On the day on which I wrote this Chapter, I saw a letter in the Lancet (27th January, 1968) from my friend Prof. J. Kleeberg of Haifa, pointing out that, unknown to Fåhraeus, an ESR test had been proposed by F. Biernacki as early as 1897.

conditions and, when such a phenomenon is found, the doctor knows that a very thorough search must be made to find the cause. There is, however, one difficulty. Not only must the test be done with extreme care but, although one skilled worker can as a rule repeat the test satisfactorily, it is very difficult to get figures that agree for the same blood tested in different laboratories.

As an alternative, considerable work has been done on rheological measurements on plasma. Harkness (1963) has described a very accurate capillary viscometer and claims that the viscosity of plasma (at fairly high shear-rates it is approximately Newtonian) gives much the same information as does the ESR with very much less personal error involved.

Much interesting work has been done, especially in Finland, by T. Somer and his colleagues on the viscosity of plasma and serum. Everyone, I think, admits that plasma is not Newtonian at low shear-rates but there has been considerable argument about serum. Most of this argument is sterile and arises from not understanding the significance of "basic equations". One should not ask "is serum Newtonian?" or even "is water Newtonian?" No real material obeys any basic equation quite perfectly. The correct form of the question is: "are deviations from Newtonian behaviour in serum greater than experimental errors under certain experimental conditions?" In fact, very careful experiments at very low rates of shear have shown significant deviations for serum from Newtonian behaviour; but at higher rates of shear serum and even plasma, may often be treated as true liquids.

Somer and his colleagues have shown that certain diseases* are associated not only with an increase in plasma viscosity, but even with a much greater viscosity-temperature change than is normal. It is not quite easy to decide whether this latter phenomenon merely reflects the fact that the higher the viscosity, the greater is the temperature dependence, or whether the two phenomena are independent.

Viscosity-concentration relations are naturally more complex at higher viscosities but again, it is not clear how far they are likely, *per se*, to prove of diagnostic value. The viscosity of normal blood is, of course, highly correlated with the concentration of red cells (haematacrit), but this is not so with most of the pathological samples.

Much work has been done on what are called "model systems". Small plastic spheres, or sometimes disks, are sheared, suspended in a liquid of almost the same density. This work gives interesting information on the

---

* Multiple myeloma (tumours arising from bone marrow); macroglobulinemia (presence of globulins of high molecular weight); ankylosing spondylitis (stiffening of ligaments of spine and joints). Except for one type of myeloma which showed a low viscosity, all other pathological conditions tended to show high viscosities.

hydrodynamics of flow and, if we remember that some of the essential characteristics of erythrocytes, such as their Kelvin-system behaviour, are missing, such researches can be helpful to haemorheologists. Rather nearer the mark are experiments with washed erythrocytes suspended in saline. But saline is not plasma and all this "simplified" work has its limitations. What is badly needed is more experiments on real native blood, difficult as these may be.

Blood vessels can be removed from dead animals or men, or even from anaesthetized living animals and the rheological properties of the walls of the vessel may be studied. But the popular trend is to picture at least the smaller blood vessels rather as holes drilled out of a matrix than as tubes surrounded by tissues. An admirable review article is that of Bergel (1966).

The elastic moduli of the vessels differ considerably as between arteries, veins, capillaries, etc., and, since many of these vessels have to withstand the pulsating flow of blood, the dynamic moduli are considerably higher than the static. The largest vessel of all, the aorta, has to have rather a low modulus, to allow for damping the surges of blood delivered by the heart. Elastic moduli have also been calculated from measured velocities at which pressure waves are transmitted; especially in the thin-walled vessels.

There is quite a considerable loss of energy ("imaginary part of the modulus") in dynamic tests. The vessel wall is divided into a number of layers having very different composition—elastin, collagen, smooth muscle, etc., so that the structure of the vessel as a whole is very complex. Collagen notably stiffens when it is stretched: smooth muscle has very different and highly complex properties, in some ways more similar to those of a Kelvin system.

The rheology in muscle is so complex and the literature so extensive that no attempt will be made to deal with this in the present book. I see that my friend Dr M. Joly has taken the same decision in his chapter on "Biorheology" in the book edited by B. Persoz (see Appendix 3).

12/Biorheology.
Part 2: Miscellaneous

The first system to be considered is protoplasm. There are two very complete review articles on this subject, one by Heilbrunn (1958) and the other by Kamiya (1959). Heilbrunn also published a much shorter article (1960) just before his tragic death in a motor accident. A considerable amount of work was published on the "viscosity" of protoplasm, in quite early times, but this was confused (as Heilbrunn has pointed out) partly because the experimenters often failed to distinguish different parts of the system, and partly because the experimental methods used almost invariably coagulated the protoplasm. Protoplasm, like blood, is coagulated when brought into contact with almost any foreign body (anti-coagulants also act in much the same way in the two systems). With regard to the former criticism, Heilbrunn makes the following comment: "One might as well make viscosity measurements of a solution and include in the value obtained the viscosity of the bottle which contained it."

Unfortunately, Heilbrunn's own rheology was by no means always sound, especially with regard to nomenclature. Moreover, the pioneer work of W. Seifriz (whatever Heilbrunn's personal views of him may have been) is not so much as mentioned. These are blemishes in an otherwise admirable monograph which includes a massive list of references.

We will not discuss the earlier attempts to measure the viscosity of protoplasm by Seifriz and others, but will confine ourselves to the three methods which have been used in comparatively recent times. The first depends on the somewhat doubtful application of Stokes' law. The calculation of his basic equation, except for the numerical coefficient (2/9) which involves quite difficult mathematics, can be simply worked out from the theory of dimensions, making a few reasonable assumptions, and this calculation is given in Appendix 2. The equation will be discussed in Chapter 14.

Here we will simply quote the equation, which applied originally to the steady rate of fall (v) of a small rigid sphere of diameter (d) under the influence of gravity (acceleration g) in a large vessel containing a Newtonian liquid of viscosity (η): $\eta = 2g\Delta\rho d^2/9v$, where $\Delta\rho$ is the difference in density between the sphere and the liquid.

The liquid phase of protoplasm is not Newtonian and the granules ("choroplasts") which are present, or small grains of starch artificially inserted, would fall far too slowly for practical measurements. However, the force can be made many times greater than that of gravity by using a centrifuge and even high centrifuge rates seem to do little damage. Various additions have been made to Stokes' basic equation but even with these, the calculated viscosities can be only approximate. This is not as serious as it sounds, since in earlier times, estimates of the consistency of protoplasm differed from that of a thick jelly to that of a liquid of low viscosity.

The second method depends on the observation of the Brownian movement of the particles as they are buffeted by the thermal agitation of the molecules. A basic equation calculated by A. Einstein and later improved by M. von Smoluchowski, relates the rate of displacement of the particles along one axis to absolute temperatures, diameter of particle and viscosity. If the granules are centrifuged to one side of the cell, the rate of return can be measured.

The third method, applicable to large masses of protoplasm, is to measure the torque on a small iron rod placed in the protoplasm in terms of a magnetic field strength. Movements of small particles of iron have also been followed. It is slightly confusing that the principal investigator in the field was A. Heilbronn, not to be mistaken for L. V. Heilbrunn, who wrote the monograph. Heilbronn found values of viscosity only a few times greater than that of water but, in many cases, the material would seem to be thixotropic.

Probably the medical man's two greatest enemies in the Western World are thrombosis and cancer. We saw in the last chapter how rheology can help in studying the former of these; unfortunately it seldom helps in cancer research. Nevertheless Heilbrunn suggests, at the end of his monograph, that there are substances which, in small concentrations, reduce protoplasmic viscosity, prevent mitosis and are anti-carcinogens; whereas at higher concentrations they increase the viscosity and act as carcinogens. Possibly further rheological measurements on protoplasm may help in this very complex field of work.

The rheology of protoplasm may also have important repercussions in connection with the study of anaesthesia.

In Britain the doctors' third most dangerous enemy is perhaps bronchitis. Patients have great difficulty in breathing because of the high consistency of the bronchial mucus. Various substances have been used to reduce this consistency and it is therefore of interest to find some way of measuring it.

This is particularly difficult (and we shall find the same difficulty later with uterine cervical mucus) because the mucus is so heterogeneous. One's first reaction would be to mix the samples thoroughly but this often destroys the very consistency that one wants to measure. Generally a compromise must be reached—some mixing but not too drastic. A good general article on work on bronchial mucus is that by White and Elmes (1960). (Valuable earlier work was done by G. Blanshard and by B. R. Hillis but these papers were published in journals probably not easily accessible to the reader.) Most of the standard types of viscometer have been used. As might be expected, the mucus is found to have a yield-value, and at higher shear-rates, either shear-thinning or what we have called rheomalaxis (pp. 34, 35). The yield-value has generally been considered to be the most useful property to measure, though it is not always made clear whether this term refers, as it should, to the stress at which appreciable flow starts, or to that at which the structure begins to be broken down. It is possible that these two stresses more or less coincide. The quantitative effects of the use of substances intended to reduce the consistency are discussed by a number of authors. G. Blanshard, J. C. White *et al*. have published phase-contrast micrographs showing the fibres in the mucus which are mainly responsible for the consistency.

White and Elmes, in the paper quoted, describe a simple apparatus for measuring "yield-values". This is made from a 20 ml glass syringe with a perforated brass block inserted above the nozzle. The yield-value is measured by placing weights on the top of the plunger and finding the load needed to start steady flow.

Rheumatic diseases are also all too prevalent and there has, for many years, been a feeling that measurements of the consistency of the synovial fluid that lubricates the joints might prove useful. Earlier researches were disappointing. There seemed to be little correlation between the consistency of the "fluid" and the condition of the patient. One difficulty, especially if human samples are used, is that it is difficult to get more than a very small sample from normal (control) subjects. When lubrication fails, the body produces more lubricant, even if this does not re-establish smooth running. Also, effectiveness as a lubricant, as we have already seen, is by no means simply related to viscosity in mechanical systems. We will not discuss the earlier and largely unsuccessful work; only one paper, published as early as 1947 in a Scandinavian journal by M. W. Ropes *et al*., should be mentioned. These authors used both a capillary viscometer with different sizes of capillary and also made an ingenious device for producing rolling and sliding friction similar to that in the joints, to measure "oiliness". A linear relation was found between the weight needed to move the "joint" and the load. The synovial fluids (bovine) were found to be non-Newtonian liquids and by engineering standards, not very good lubricants. Some years later (1954), working with medical colleagues at the Royal Free Hospital, London, Ropes found empirically that the apparent viscosity of human "fluids" was linearly related to the logarithm of the stress. No correlation could be found with the pathological conditions of the patients.

Recently, however, Myers, Negami and White (1966) have been more successful, using a torsion pendulum "rheometer".* The fluids have both elastic and viscous properties, dynamic viscosities and elasticity moduli being calculated. In the low frequency region, the "fluid" behaves as a viscous liquid but at high frequencies (corresponding to rapid movements of the joints) elastic properties preponderate. Although the addition of hydro-cortisone did not directly affect these properties, injections into patients show-ing certain types of abnormality increased both the dynamic viscosity and modulus of the synovial fluid.

Many workers have studied joint stiffness. A good review is given by Barnett *et al.* (1961). After this article was published, Johns and Wright (1964) studied stresses and strains in the human finger joint. The stress-strain curves showed some hysteresis and a rheological model of a joint, identical with Schofield and Scott Blair's flour-dough model, was proposed.

The properties of bone have also been studied, perhaps rather more from the engineering ("strength of materials") viewpoint than from that of the rheologist. An excellent general summary is given by Bell (1956). In a later paper, Currey (1964) claimed that bone is a two-phase system like fibre-glass and, like some concretes, is "pre-stressed". How this comes about is not understood.

At about the time of the start of the Second World War, Dr H. Waller, working in a hospital in the London area, was worried by the number of cases of mastitis and breast ulcers in lactating women. These conditions were often associated with engorgement and Dr Waller found that, by manual removal of the pre-natal secretion, pressure was reduced and subsequent troubles often averted. He suggested to me that the engorgement might be caused by a yield-value ("solid property") in the milk.

A simple viscometer was constructed consisting of two fairly wide vertical glass tubes joined at the bottom by a horizontal capillary. The liquid was forced up into one side of this viscometer and the subsequent rate of fall was timed. For a Newtonian liquid, the rate of fall is always proportional to the head of liquid, so that a plot of the logarithm of the head

---

* *Rheometer* is a useful general term for an instrument that measures rheological proper-ties; not necessarily only viscosity.

should be linear with time. Although the viscosities of the samples varied greatly, they were all found to be almost Newtonian and it was concluded that the engorgement was caused, not by any rheological anomalies in the secretion but by faults in the operation of the breast itself. It now seems likely that the improvements effected were due rather to Dr Waller's general organization of the hospital than to his manual removal of the pre-natal secretion.

Space does not permit reference to work on many other medical and biological problems; but, before concluding this chapter, some account must be given of experiments in a very topical and important field; the relationship between rheological properties of mucus from the female uterine cervix and fertility. But so much has now been published about this that only a very superficial summary can be given here.

It probably started with the cows. Like most mammals other than primates, cows show a period of "heat" or oestrus, just before ovulation occurs and it is only then that they can be fertilized, either by natural or artificial methods.

The cow has a very regular three-week cycle and this, combined with certain characteristic modes of behaviour, generally make it quite easy for the farmer to recognize the condition. However, there are occasions, generally when the climate is extreme—hot or cold—when ovulation occurs and the cow could be fertilized although there are no obvious signs of oestrus. One of the changes which takes place as a result of alterations in the balance of the sex hormones in oestrus, dioestrus ("not oestrus") and in pregnancy is a marked alteration in the rheological properties of the slimy mucus which is formed in the small passage (cervix) between the vagina and the uterus. In oestrus, this mucus is very plentiful, of low consistency and shows marked flow-elasticity and spinability. In dioestrus, the mucus is scanty, more gelatinous and almost devoid of flow-elasticity and spinability. For many years now, it has been possible to measure all these properties except the last. The difficulty with spinability was that, in order to draw a thread, one must be able to attach the mucus to some sort of grips out of which it cannot slip. Unfortunately mucus will slip out of almost anything except human fingers! Recently however, my colleagues and I have described a very simple apparatus for drawing threads of mucus held, at the suggestion of my Israeli friend Dr Y. Weis, in two pairs of Bassequer eye forceps (Burnett et al. 1967).

Some twenty-five years previously we had invented a simple little device called (perhaps unfortunately) "the oestroscope", which measured elastic recoil on release of pressure in an empty capillary. We also used various types of capillary viscometer to measure a kind of overall consistency. Consistency is fairly high at the time of the cycle furthest from oestrus; but continues to rise well into pregnancy. For cows showing no pathological conditions of the genital tract, we could establish a value of consistency which, when exceeded, was diagnostic of pregnancy. Since the usual hormonal tests for pregnancy do not work for cows, there was no way of knowing whether a cow was pregnant until the veterinarian could feel the foetal membranes *per rectum*, usually at about 40 days after conception. Our test, which is most fully described in a paper by Scott Blair and Glover (1957), gave a correct diagnosis for pregnant cows after 27–29 days in 95% of cases.

Tests for non-pregnant cows were not so successful: only 75% for cows which had been mated, but 95% for those that could not possibly be pregnant. The reason for the low figure of 75% was fairly clear. At 28 days, the cows were pregnant; but, by the time the veterinarian could examine them at 40 days, he found, in some cases, no foetus and our test also showed a negative result. The test has not been widely used by the farmer, partly because taking the sample in early pregnancy from the cervix, is almost as skilled a job as feeling for a foetal membrane and partly, no doubt, because he would sooner know after 40 days that he is really likely to get a calf than be told, at 28 days that his cow is pregnant but may lose her foetus. (Here, as someone facetiously pointed out, cows differ from duchesses!) The test has been used, and I hope will continue to be used, especially in Israel, for research into the causes of early foetal deaths.

Rheology, fortunately, knows no frontiers and it was in Egypt that it was shown that the above findings for cows also apply to buffaloes. In some countries, the latter are at least as important as cows in the dairy industry.

Meanwhile, this work naturally interested the gynaecologists and others concerned with problems of fertility. As elsewhere in this book, we must make a somewhat arbitrary choice of references. It would seem best to restrict ourselves to two teams, though many others have done valuable work. A somewhat out-of-date article by the author summarized this work—Scott Blair (1952).

Clift (1947), Clift *et al.* (1950) and Clift and Hart (1953) carried out experiments on mucus from women and came to much the same conclusions as those reached by earlier workers on bovine mucus. Only very small amounts of mucus are available and Clift invented a micro-version of the oestroscope which he called "the menstroscope" (though this really indicates ovulation and not menstruation). (It must be remembered that cows are fortunate enough not to menstruate and that women have no oestrus period. The dates in the cycle for cows are therefore generally given from the time of oestrus or ovulation which immediately follows; whereas for women the zero date is the start of menstruation.) Various conditions of the mucus were found by Clift to be associated not only with pregnancy but also with certain pathological conditions.

Clift sometimes used "blobs" of secretion moving along a capillary, a method with which I and my colleagues had no success; but I. Braun-Halperin in Israel found this method quite feasible.

With normal non-pregnant women, the "consistency" passed through a minimum at about the 15th day of the cycle (at ovulation) and showed signs of a less marked minimum when samples were taken as near to menstruation as was possible. Consistencies for samples from pregnant women tested were higher than all those for non-pregnant women. However, with women, hormone tests for pregnancy are so reliable at such an early stage that a mucus test is unlikely to be of practical importance.

In later years, a number of other pre- and ante-natal clinics organized rheological tests on mucus. The most fully published were those from Exeter (England) by Harvey and her colleagues (1948, 1954, 1960). These workers made careful quantitative comparisons between measurements of consistency and flow-elasticity and other methods, such as the examination of the "P.L." (palm-leaf) structures of sodium chloride crystals in dried secretions, glucose paper, basal temperatures etc.

In the later papers, they were more concerned with the penetration of sperm into the mucus. It has been suggested that the remarkable properties of the mucus at the time of ovulation aid the sperm finding their way through the cervix and that the thick gelatinous secretions of pregnancy tend to protect the uterus from being entered. The semen does not itself penetrate the mucus. The sperm leave the seminal fluid and swim independently through the mucus.

Mr F. A. Glover and I, when we were working together (Glover and Scott Blair 1966) showed that, if untreated bull semen stored for the shortest possible time at the optimal temperature of 20°C, is subjected to a sudden rise of temperature up to 40°C, before the sperm die, there is a rise in apparent viscosity, believed to be due to their activation by the heat. After this, like over-active businessmen, they die. The viscosity then falls, finally increasing again as the dead sperm bunch together like rafts in a stream.

When sperm swim in semen they are not distributed at random but form up in shoals, rather like fish. There is also considerable synchronization of the waving of their long tails. If such a system is sheared, the sperm will be orientated along the streamlines and, if shearing is suddenly stopped, they will take time to re-establish their natural configuration. Mr Glover, continuing this work after my retirement, has found that the rate at which this configuration is re-established can be measured using suitable optical methods and is correlated with the "motility" of the sperm. This motility is generally assessed subjectively by those concerned with artificial insemination and a good quantitative test would be useful both in practice and also for research purposes.

13/Psycho-Rheology: Measurement of Sensations: Craftsmanship

As soon as it is proved that two sensations can be equal without being identical, psychophysics will be established.—H. Bergson.

Of course Bergson was quite convinced that this could never be done. His whole book: "Essai sur les données immédiates de la conscience", published in 1889, was directed to show what he believed to be the fallacy of some of his contemporaries who claimed to be measuring sensations. It is clearly impossible to measure things unless it is possible that two of them at least will give the same measure.

These arguments may seem at first sight to be highly academic; nevertheless, to industrial rheologists, especially those working in traditional industries, they have immediate practical significance. In these industries, and in some cases even in those dealing with newly-invented synthetic products, the rheologists' first task is often to try to replace the subjective assessment by the craftsman of some "property" such as consistency, body, tack, etc., by means of instrumental measurements. Was Bergson right? Is this a hopeless task?

First, we had better discuss what Bergson means by "psycho-physics" and what is really meant by "measurement". We must go back as far as 1834, when Weber found experimentally, that the just noticeable difference in some stimulus, say a light beam, is proportional to the physical intensity of the radiation. This is an experimental finding, many times since found to be approximately true, and not involving any theory. Bergson would not have called this "psycho-physics". Many years later (about 1850 but published in 1860) Fechner further developed this work, making various assumptions. First he assumed that a sensation (S) is made up of a number of small increments (ΔS) corresponding to the smallest differences of stimulus (ΔE) and that all the ΔS's are equal to one another; or $\Delta S/\Delta E = C/E$, where C is a constant. Then it is assumed that ΔS and ΔE are so small that they may be replaced by dS and dE, and, by integration: $S = C \ln (E/Q)$, where Q is a constant.

This is going far further than Weber and it is therefore wrong to call this the "Weber-Fechner equation". In fact, Bergson criticized every assumption that Fechner made. He maintained that one cannot equate increments of sensation: they are not "quantities", that it is therefore impossible to make them to correspond to increments of stimulus, and that these increments are not infinitesimal and that the equation, even if it had any meaning, should therefore not be integrated.

His opponents, notably Delboeuf, claimed that the proof of the pudding is in the eating. It is experimentally possible to construct a scale of sensations which is, within reasonable limits of error, reproducible for different normal subjects. For example, a subject is shown two rings, one of a light grey and the other a darker grey. He can adjust the depths of greyness of a third ring and is asked to do this in such a way that it lies half way between the original pair. From such experiments it was possible to show that there is a logarithmic relation between stimulus and sensation and to find values, not only for the Weber constant, but also for the Fechner constant.* Plateau, on the other hand, concluded from his experiments with other stimuli, that the relationship was doubly logarithmic and it seemed to be a question to be decided, either by further experiments, or it could be that the Fechner equation holds for some kinds of experiment and Plateau's for others.

It is such attempts to measure sensations that Bergson called "psycho-physics" and condemned as futile. He considered that the subjects were merely guessing, with greater or lesser success, the probable intensity of the stimuli.

We must now leave these interesting early controversies, of which I have given such a sketchy description, to see how the problem has been tackled in our own times. We shall see in a moment that, strangely enough, a very similar difference of opinion has recently arisen between psycho-physicists.

The scene here moves from France and Belgium to America and Britain. (Just before the Second World War, a Committee of the British Association for the Advancement of Science held lengthy discussions to try to decide whether sensations really are measurable, but could reach no definite conclusion.)

At Harvard University, S. S. Stevens has very greatly extended the kind of experiments done by Delboeuf and by Plateau; but first, very properly, he has raised the question "What do we mean by 'measurement'?"

Stevens defines "measurement" as "the assignment of numerals to things so as to represent facts and conventions about them". And he very properly points out that "when description gives way to measurement, calculation

---

* This constant would have the dimensions of a sensation, whatever that may mean!

replaces debate". (For his earlier work see Stevens 1951.) Stevens proposed four types of measurement, which can easily be memorized from the French word for "black": NOIR.

1. *Nominal.* Most of us would hardly call these measurements. For example, soldiers or prisoners are given numbers to replace their names. To the initiated, the number does, of course, give information about the individual but tells one nothing about the relationships between the individuals, unless allocated in some special way.

2. *Ordinal.* We have already come across Mohs' hardness scale. Each member is harder than its neighbour on one side and softer than its neighbour on the other side; but, until correlations were found with indentation data, there was no evidence of any law regulating the intervals between them.

3. *Interval.* Here we have equality of intervals but no meaningful zero. One cannot convert from one scale to another simply by multiplying by a factor: e.g. Fahrenheit and Centigrade temperature scales. (In his later work, Stevens sub-divides this category into linear and logarithmic interval scales, which really correspond to the Fechner and the Plateau equations.)*

4. *Ratio* scales include measurements of most physical properties in absolute units—lengths, masses, temperatures (Kelvin scale) etc.

One of the most important points made by Stevens is that most ordinary statistical techniques cannot logically be applied to the first two types of measurement. In practice, of course, this rule is often broken. The psychologists, and I myself as a rheologist, have used multiple factor analysis (which depends on correlation coefficients) to express data from subjective assessments in what are certainly only ordinal scales (see below). But, like Delboeuf and Plateau, we seem to get away with it! Bergson would say, no doubt, that the subjects are making good guesses about the equality of the differences in stimuli. Stevens' work would seem, at first sight, to have settled the Bergson-Delboeuf dispute. Bergson did not define the term "measure". One can "measure" sensations on an ordinal, but not on an interval, still less a ratio scale.

Strangely enough, however, a rather similar debate has recently taken place between Stevens and M. Treisman (now in Reading, England). Stevens (1957) defined two types of stimulus, which he calls "prothetic" and "metathetic". The former are quantitative and concerned with the question "how much?", while the latter are qualitative and are concerned with the question "of what

---

* It is not always easy, in reading Stevens' papers, to distinguish his use of single and of double logarithmic equations. He sometimes writes "logarithmic" without making it clear whether the equation is of the type $y = e^x$ or $y = x^a$.

kind?" Stevens found that, in the former case, Plateau's double logarithmic equation holds, whereas in the latter, one can use the single logarithm of Fechner.

Treisman (1962) (who has also published several papers criticizing Stevens in the *Quart. J. exper. Psychol.*, to which Stevens has replied) returns to a position not so very different from that of Bergson. He claims that no experiment can distinguish between the two equations. The answer we get will depend on how we define the "units" of sensation. We *learn* to make ratio comparisons for prothetic stimuli but not for metathetic. (I am here in a difficulty: the pitch of a sound is a metathetic mode, yet we surely learn very quickly how to recognize octaves and other ratios on an "even tempered scale" if we are at all musical.) The significance of all this to rheology is obvious; and yet very few experiments appear to have been described. Harper and Stevens (1964) compared the assessment of hardness of rubber-like materials, handled by blindfolded subjects, with readings on a sphere-hardness tester. The force-indentation curves were not linear. Subjects were asked how many times one sample was harder than another. A double logarithmic law was found to hold satisfactorily (with a slope of about 0·3), except at the upper and lower ends, where the curves became sigmoid.

Stevens and Guirao (1964) asked subjects to compare the viscosity of silicones by (a) shaking or turning a bottle, (b) stirring with a rod (blindfolded) and (c) by vision. "If liquid A seems five times as viscous as B, give it five times the score." So long as viscosities were judged, the double logarithmic equation held well (the slope was between 0·4 and 0·5) but, when asked to judge fluidities, the results were not so good.

A few other researches should perhaps be mentioned briefly. In 1959, L-E Fryklöf carried out somewhat similar tests with cosmetic creams and confirmed a simple logarithmic relation. E. A. Grawmeyer and M. C. Pfund, in 1943, found good correlations between subjective assessments of apple sauce and cream fillings tested on a line-spread consistometer (see Chapter 14). M. Naudet *et al.* have made extensive studies of the spreading of butter (see Chapter 16). Matz (1962) discusses the subjective assessments of quality of various foodstuffs. Saunders (1948) discusses brushability of paints. Szczesniak and her colleagues have published many excellent papers on foodstuffs: it is hard to know which to quote. Perhaps the most accessible to the reader concerned with psycho-rheology would be Szczesniak (1963).

Apart from these researches, I know of little else in the way of "psycho-rheological" experiments other than those done in my own laboratory (the work of Drake is somewhat different and will be discussed later). Our results were published in many diverse journals but I wrote up the whole subject in my book "A Survey of General and Applied Rheology". However, since this is now out of print, I will give a brief summary here.

Just over thirty years ago, I was working on the rheological properties of flour doughs, with Dr R. K. Schofield at Rothamsted and in co-operation with Dr P. Halton at the (then) British Flour Millers' Research Association. We were attempting to correlate the properties of our doughs as measured on rheometers with the quality as assessed by an expert baker and it soon became evident that dealing with expert judgments is the job of the psychologist and not the rheologist. We were extremely fortunate in having the help, for a short time, of one of Europe's leading psychologists, Prof. D. Katz, who had had to leave Nazi Germany and had not yet taken up his Chair in Sweden. We studied the doughs and Katz studied the bakers. His results were most interesting (Katz 1937). Among his conclusions we find: "The psychological properties *e.g.* body, spring or elasticity *etc.* do not correspond to the physical properties of viscosity, elasticity *etc.* but are the result of a complicated co-operation of the different senses of the skin, muscles, sinews, joints *etc.* Thus the property called elasticity or spring by the baker does not correspond to the physical elasticity but is more accurately expressed by the viscosity/ elasticity ratio" (i.e. the relaxation time). In spite of working with unusually intelligent bakers, Katz concludes: "The reliability of a baker's subjective judgments concerning dough properties is not great . . . the judgments of several bakers on the same dough often show wide differences. A baker may not be very successful in distinguishing various doughs whose differences, *e.g.* of elasticity and viscosity, can be defined in an objective way."

L. B. Crossland and H. H. Favor compared measurements of "firmness" of bread using a compression instrument, with assessments made by 20 subjects, but did not discuss the psycho-physical equations. When I first went to Reading to work on dairy products (1937), I was asked especially to investigate what the cheese-makers and graders were really judging by when they assess the "body" and similar properties of cheese. It was clear that I needed a psychologist colleague to help me to tackle this problem. In the course of fifteen years or so during which the programme was occupying me, I had three psychologists with me: first, Dr Valda Coppen; then, on her marriage, Dr R. Harper (who has the additional advantage of being qualified in physics); and finally Dr D. Sheppard, though Dr Sheppard spent more of his time on consumer preference and other problems.

It seemed to me that the first thing to find out was how accurately cheese-makers and others could judge differences in the viscosity of highly viscous liquids and the elastic moduli of Hookean bodies comparable to (Cheddar) cheese in firmness. We found a bitumen (Californian) which was very nearly

G

Newtonian and which could be diluted with oil to make small cylinders differing in viscosity. For our elastic cylinders initially we used rubber but later we had small steel springs with plastic disks on the ends, the springs being covered by a "bandage". Many experiments were done in which subjects squeezed two cylinders, one in each hand at constant temperature, then changed hands and squeezed again (to eliminate differences in hand-strength). Subjects were told to try to use about the same pressures throughout. These experiments showed that viscosity differences of about 10% could be discriminated at above a chance level and elastic moduli about three times as accurately. There was no evidence of any superiority on the part of cheesemakers, or indeed any other category except routine analysts, who, doubtless because they were used to doing rather monotonous experiments without boredom or fatigue, scored rather better than the rest.

It would appear from Fig. 13.1 that the curves plotting the logarithm of the difference in elastic modulus and viscosity against percentage correct answers are linear; in fact, over a wider range, they are sigmoid in form. Dr R. Harper analysed similar curves when he was working with me, by means of a method known as "Probit Analysis".

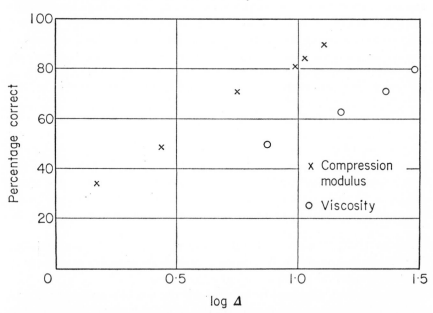

Fig 13.1 Threshold curves for Elastic Moduli and Viscosities (Δ is percentage difference in viscosity or modulus of the pair). (Reproduced with permission from: *Proceedings of the Royal Society of London*, Series B, No. 850, vol. 128, pp. 109–125, 1939)

This result at first sight seemed easy to explain. Presumably, the subjects judged the firmness of an elastic spring by how *far* it compressed under the applied pressure and the viscosity of the bitumen by how *fast* it flowed. It is understandable that a "static" judgment should be more accurate than that on a flowing system.

But we were soon disillusioned. If we asked a subject to compare a spring in one hand with a bitumen in the other during a time fixed by a metronome, only a few physicists (who knew that it is impossible to say that a viscosity is greater or less than an elastic modulus), had any difficulty in making a decision and a very simple equation relating viscosity, elastic modulus and time of squeezing was found to hold.

A long series of experiments which cannot be described here in detail (see Scott Blair and Coppen (1939) and Scott Blair *et al.* (1947)), using not only elastic and viscous materials but also substances which obey the Nutting equation (see Chapter 9) led us to the conclusion that firmness was judged neither by strain (γ) nor by rate of change of strain ($d\gamma/dt$) but by some entity intermediate between the two; i.e. a fractional differential. Only a much simplified version of the theory can be given here but it should be mentioned because it bears on the fundamental question (for many rheologists) as to how experts judge consistency in handling materials. When we write "$d\gamma/dt$", the "t" refers to the ordinary time of physics: "Newtonian time". I have been quite wrongly accused of proposing to discard the use of this time-scale, the basis of so many well-established physical laws, by some other time-scale. This I have never done. What I pointed out was that, when human beings judge the properties of materials by handling them, they do not have a Newtonian clock in their heads! Therefore, if, *rightly*, one uses Newtonian time to describe their judgments, one must not expect simple relations in terms of whole-number differentiations. Physical properties, such as elastic moduli and viscosities are measured by a single magnitude. Such subjectively assessed "properties" as "body", "texture", etc. may well have intermediate dimensions (see Scott Blair and Caffyn (1949)) and must be measured by two (not independent) magnitudes. The proof of the pudding is in the eating. For materials obeying the Nutting equation with $\beta = 1$, ($\psi = \tau\gamma^{-1}t^k$), the value of k could be determined both by compressing cylinders on a rheometer under constant stress and plotting log γ *vs.* log t and also from a statistical analysis of a large number of subjective "squeezing" tests. The values obtained were found to agree within the limits of experimental error. Unfortunately, no further work has been done along these lines for many years. I am including a brief account in this book in the hopes that some rheologist may find in our earlier work, some ideas for further research.

One point was quite clear in all our experiments. The "inexpert" is quite prepared to "analyse" his sensations, e.g. to distinguish between the firmness, springiness, crumbliness of cheese, whereas the expert finds it very hard to give more than a single judgment of overall quality. This, to him, is what some psychologists would call a *Gestalt*: something greater than the sum of its parts and not analysable. We must not call the "know-how" of the expert "instinctive" because it is not inborn; it is learned and subconsciously stored. Such "learned instincts" (to use a contradiction in terms) are generally called "schemata".

Following our work on cheese, my colleagues Dr J. H. Prentice and Dr D. Sheppard studied the "spreadability" of butter. Large numbers of housewives and later a trained panel, were asked to score butters for "spreadability" and also for other properties. Very high correlation coefficients were found, with a number of rheological tests, the best being the use of a specially designed extruder rheometer, in which butter is forced through a short wide capillary at a constant rate, the required force being recorded on a chart.

All these tests, like the cheese tests, were subjected to Factor Analysis. This method does not give unique solutions and is therefore not popular with the statisticians. Nevertheless they have not yet provided us with an alternative. Where these researches were done, the method also had the disadvantage of involving very lengthy computations: but now, with a computer, this could be avoided.

The principle is quite simple. Suppose we have N tests, some rheological and some subjective judgments. If we break Stevens' rules about using statistics on ordinal scales, we can work out the correlation of each with every other test and this would seem to give N^2 correlation coefficients. We can write these in the form of a square matrix, leaving blank the diagonal components, since the correlation of a test with itself must be unity, excluding errors. But we can also cut out half the remaining table, since the correlation of A with B is the same as that of B with A. This leaves us with $N/2 (N - 1)$ components.

But it is unlikely that there is no "order" among these components and the test-matrix may generally be reduced to a simpler factor-matrix describing the relationships in terms of a few "factors", or imaginary tests which in our case (but not in psychology) were always orthogonal, i.e. completely independent of one another. If not more than three of these are worth considering, solid models may be made showing how all the tests—objective and subjective—are related to one another. For example, for Cheddar cheese, we used firmness, springiness and (probably) crumbliness.

The last work to be considered in this somewhat long chapter has been done partly in America (especially by A. S. Szczesniak and her colleagues) and partly in Sweden by Drake. The latter is especially concerned with the toughness of food in relation to mastication. Some of this work is pure rheology and is not concerned with psychological judgments but a special feature of it has been Drake's study, by sensitive electronic devices, of the sounds made by the jaws (see Drake 1962, 1963, 1965). He has also made a detailed study of the mechanism of chewing food from the odontological and anatomical points of view.

Part II
Rheological Measurements

14/Materials of Low Consistency

a/Capillary viscometers

Many research workers who are not rheologists (and I was, for a short time, one of them) when they are faced with a problem involving measurements of "viscosity", immediately think of an Ostwald viscometer. Indeed, when I was a student, it was the only viscometer that I was taught to use. The Ostwald viscometer, shown in Fig. 14.1, depends on the measurement of the time taken for a given volume of liquid to fall through a standard vertical capillary. The calculation for the equation of flow of a liquid through a capillary is given in Appendix 2; but, even without this, it is clear that the rate of fall of the liquid will depend as much on the density (ρ) as on the viscosity (η), so that the time of fall is, in fact, proportional to the ratio η/ρ. Since this ratio is often all we need to know, it has been given a special name: the *kinematic** *viscosity* (v). Since viscosity has the dimensions $ML^{-1}T^{-1}$ and density, ML^{-3}, v must have dimensions L^2T^{-1}.

Ostwald viscometers are used for the very accurate measurement of viscosity of Newtonian liquids and, for this purpose, various "corrections" have to be made. For example, the liquid accelerates when it enters the capillary: the shape of the entrance to the capillary is important: a correction must be made because the capillary is not very long in relation to its diameter, etc. But, since

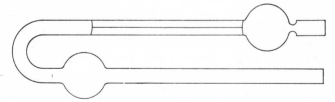

Fig. 14.1 Ostwald Viscometer

---

* There is a slight confusion here in nomenclature. In order to distinguish η from v, the former is sometimes called "the dynamic viscosity". But this term is also used, as we have seen, for the viscosity calculated from the imaginary part of the complex modulus: η is better called "the steady state viscosity".

in this book we are not concerned with very accurate measures of viscosity, these corrections will not be discussed, nor will the many modifications of the Ostwald viscometer. (For a good elementary account of these, the reader is referred to the book by A. Dinsdale and F. Moore, see Appendix 3.)

What is not generally realized is that the Ostwald viscometer and its modifications are *not* suitable for non-Newtonian systems. There are difficulties in using any capillary viscometer for such systems, as we shall see in a moment, but the Ostwald type is particularly unsuitable because the "head" (i.e. the pressure) is falling continuously: so, if the viscosity varies with pressure, only a rather arbitrary "average" viscosity will be measured.

Many designs of capillary viscometers have been used to obviate this difficulty. One very simple method is to cut the bottom off two pipettes, bend round the remainder of the wide exit tubes at right-angles, and attach a horizontal capillary between them. As the tested material flows under an applied air-pressure from one bulb into the other, the levels can be kept constant by rotating the whole apparatus. The air displaced by the incoming material is passed through a very narrow capillary, behind which is a sensitive manometer. Since air is itself Newtonian (at low rates of flow) the pressure on this manometer measures directly the rate of flow of the material. The experiment is repeated at a series of pressures.

This type of apparatus also has the advantage that it at least partially meets a more serious criticism of all capillary rheometers. In capillary flow, the stress and shear-rate are at their greatest at the wall of the tube and fall to zero at the centre (see Appendix 2), so measurements are not being made at a constant shear-rate. With the above arrangement, however, if a wide range of overall pressures is used, the "average apparent viscosity" at each pressure can be meaningfully related to the pressure.

When only small samples are available, an alternative method (used in work on blood and plasma) is to bend two rather wide tubes at right-angles and attach a horizontal capillary between them. A small column of the material to be tested, all of which is contained in the horizontal part of the apparatus, is timed, flowing through the capillary, by the position of the meniscus in one of the wide tubes. This tube must be wide enough to ensure that surface-tension forces are insignificant and that the hydrodynamic resistance may be neglected by comparison with that in the capillary; but it must be narrow enough to give a good clear meniscus reading. Suitable electronic recording can make such an instrument really quite accurate (e.g. Harkness 1963). The direction of flow may be reversed either by applying pressure at alternate sides, or by using suction. Another method for small samples, often ascribed to E. C. Bingham and H. Murray but I believe first proposed as early as 1914 by A. Pochettino, is to measure the decelerating rate in a gradually filling capillary under constant pressure. The equations for this and for the corresponding "emptying" capillary will be given in Appendix 2.

Such methods are seldom accurate but are useful for biological systems when samples are sparse and variations in consistency are so great that high accuracy is not important (e.g. cervical mucus). It should never be forgotten that most systems of this kind change their consistency as they are sheared so that it is a process (and an arbitrary one at that) rather than a property that is being measured.

b/Coaxial cylinder viscometers

These are sometimes known by the generic name of "Couette viscometers" because an early and well-known form was devised by a Frenchman of that name. There are, in fact, many varieties. The principle is that the material is sheared between two cylinders, one of which is rotated at a constant speed and the other is attached to a torsion wire or other device for measuring the torque. In place of rotation, the former cylinder may be oscillated, preferably with a sinusoidal motion. In this way, a complex modulus may be measured (see Chapter 7). If the width of the gap between the cylinders is small compared with their radii, the rate of shear may be taken as almost constant. But it is evident that such instruments must be very accurately made. As early as 1889, the Russian worker T. Shvedov* described an apparatus, later improved, in 1926, by E. Hatschek and R. S. Jane, in which the shear modulus of elastic liquids could also be measured.

As is the case with capillary rheometers, there are "corrections" to be made, either by modifying the apparatus or the equation, for coaxial cylinder viscometers. The principal trouble is with the "end effect" at the bottom of the cylinder. This is sometimes hollowed out to hold a bubble of air; or baffle plates are used. (The reader is again referred to A. Dinsdale and F. Moore. The formula for coaxial cylinders will be given in Appendix 2.)

An interesting point was made by Sir Geoffrey Taylor (1936). He calculated that, when the inner cylinder is rotated, turbulence appears at a much lower Reynolds' number than when the outer cylinder is rotated. For work at high rates of shear, this can be important.

Flow-birefringence hardly comes within the scope of elementary rheology, but mention should be made of it, since, especially some years ago, its measurement in transparent materials, sheared between coaxial cylinders,

---

* Often written with the German transliteration "Schwedoff".

was fairly common. Although the results gave quite interesting information about certain systems, it is much less widely used than it used to be, no doubt because it is difficult to relate the data to molecular structure unless one is sure that one is dealing with molecules of simple shape, such as rigid rods. The principle is that a beam of polarized monochromatic light is passed vertically through the material as it is sheared between the cylinders. This beam is observed between crossed Nicol prisms. It now consists of two components differently polarized and travelling at different speeds. A cross is seen whose orientation indicates the difference between the alignment of the molecules and that of the streamlines. The emergent light is elliptically polarized and is re-converted to plane polarized light by the rotation of a birefringent plate. Two quantities are normally measured: the "angle of isocline" (or its complement, the "angle of extinction") and the amount of birefringence itself which is defined as the difference between the refractive indices. For Newtonian liquids, birefringence is proportional to shear-rate and the angle of isocline is 45°. Good descriptions of the method are to be found in Edsall (1942) and Signer (1954).

c/Cone-cone and cone-plate viscometers

If even more constant rates of shear are required, the material may be sheared between two very wide-angled cones or between a cone and a horizontal plate. The latter is rotated or oscillated and the torque on the upper cone is measured. For small angles, the increasing width of gap as one moves from the centre outwards, just balances the increasing speed. Various baffle systems have been used to prevent samples of rather low consistency from spilling over.

It is sometimes important also to measure "normal forces" (see Chapter 6), i.e. forces which usually tend to push the cone upwards, away from the plate. K. Weissenberg, who attaches great importance to the tensorial nature of stress and strain, felt that an instrument was needed that would measure the components of force at all angles. He has gradually developed what is certainly the most general and complete all-purpose rheometer, well known as the "rheogoniometer". This measures tangential and normal forces, either in rotation or oscillation.

d/Falling, rolling and sliding spheres

The original "falling sphere viscometer" depends on Stokes' law (see Chapter 12 and Appendix 2). This equation holds only when a rigid sphere is falling freely in a very large quantity of material. Various corrections have been proposed to allow for the effects of the walls and bottom end of the containing cylinder but none of these is really satisfactory. In general, the method is best used for comparative measurements and not for absolute viscosity determinations. If the fall of the sphere cannot be observed visually (opaque materials) and if the sphere is of steel, its presence can be registered electro-magnetically as it passes between two encircling coils.

The method sounds simple and has had its uses (e.g. for heather honey) and, as will be seen later, it is easy to derive the form of the equation of fall of the sphere from purely dimensional considerations. But, in fact, the stress conditions round the sphere are very complex and the calculation of the appropriate constant involves not only difficult mathematics but is even then open to controversy. The rate of rising spheres, with a density less than that of the material tested, and even of air bubbles (which are not spherical) has also been measured.

In a well-known German instrument, a sphere rolls or slides down the side of an inclined tube only slightly wider than the sphere; and in other instruments, spheres are forced through the material in a containing tube under pressure. There is, of course, no possible application of the Stokes equation to such instruments, useful as they may be in practice.

Behar and Frei (1955), in Israel, described a most ingenious rheometer in which the fall of a minute steel sphere is magnetically controlled, being pulled in any desired direction. The elasticity of elastic liquids may be measured by drawing the ball sideways and then, on release, measuring the recoil. Viscosities can, of course, also be measured. This instrument is particularly useful when only very small samples are available.

e/Empirical methods

It is sometimes hard to say whether a rheometer should be described as an orifice or a capillary instrument. Everything from a very narrow orifice to rather short capillaries has been used. Perhaps the first viscometer ever to be described is that of Lomonosov, in 1751, which resembles in many ways some of the commercial viscometers still used for oils. Most oils, except the heaviest, are Newtonian fluids and it should not matter what type of viscometer is used to measure their viscosity. But an orifice instrument, as E. W. J. Mardles and A. G. Ward* have pointed out, is liable to measure density rather than

---

* In a paper read at a Conference but unpublished because of the war.

viscosity. They quote E. C. Bingham as saying that in the Engler (oil) viscometer, "the kinetic energy correction amounts to over 90% of the total energy
expended".

A. Pochettino, in the work already quoted, published as early as 1914,
described an apparatus in which an inner cylinder is drawn downwards by a
weight through a material (pitch) contained in a concentric outer cylinder.
This method can be used only when the viscosity of the sample is high enough
to prevent serious leakage through the hole in the bottom of the outer cylinder
which is needed to allow for the passage of the thread holding the weight.
There is a "micro" form of this method in which a needle falls within a
vertical tube.

For liquids of lower viscosity, some variant of the Gardner Mobilometer is
often used. In such instruments, the internal cylinder or disk is perforated
with holes through which the liquid can flow. Either the weight of the cylinder
provides the force, or additional weights may be added. This method has been
widely used for testing paints.

P. G. Nutting derived his equation which we have already discussed to
apply to data obtained by withdrawing a rectangular plate upwards, through
the material contained in a cylinder, by means of a weight suspended from
pulleys. This may almost be regarded as a fundamental method, since the
material is subjected to a simple shear.

Mardles (1946) describes a rather similar method. A rectangular glass or
metal plate is hung in a liquid from the free end of a horizontal glass or
quartz "beam". The liquid surrounding the plate is in a graduated tube and
runs out from the bottom. The drag on the plate is measured by the deflection
of the beam. The apparatus is suitable for greases and paints.

Quite a few commercial viscometers operate on rather similar principles.
The reader is referred to the book by Van Wazer *et al.* quoted in Appendix 3
which gives a description of those available in 1963.

A useful empirical method for materials of about the consistency of batter
is known as the "line-spread consistometer". Concentric circles are marked on
a flat plate and the sample is placed in a hollow cylinder standing on the
middle of the plate. On removing the cylinder, the material slumps out across
the "target" and the diameter of the circle where it comes to rest is recorded.
For materials of rather higher consistency, the whole plate, with the slumped
sample on it, may be lifted through a known height and then dropped, perhaps several times. This causes the sample to spread further across the "target".

It goes without saying that *all* measurements of viscosity or apparent
viscosity must be made at constant temperature, since the temperature co-

efficient for viscosity is so very high. Elasticity is, in general, much less temperature dependent.

It is hoped that, from this and the subsequent chapter, the "beginner" in rheology may get some ideas about methods which might be suitable for testing the materials in which he is interested. Some of the relevant equations are given in Appendix 2.

15/Materials of High Consistency

Methods for testing more or less solid materials are not so easy to classify as are those used for liquids or near-liquids. The principles involved are generally very simple, such as the extension of rods or bending of beams, or very complex and completely empirical.

Creep tests are important for metals (see Appendix 1) and also for some non-metals such as plastics. In these tests, a rod or "wire" of the material is held under a constant load* (at a constant temperature) for a long period of time and the extension is followed. This is quite a complicated process so far as the sample is concerned, partly because, as discussed in Chapter 3, the sample gets thinner as it lengthens and the total volume by no means always remains constant. Apart from lack of uniformity of cross-section, which is often prevented by work-hardening at the narrow points, the tensile stress (force per unit area) increases if the load is kept constant. At least two methods have been proposed to keep the stress approximately constant. One is by means of a hyperbolic weight hung in a liquid on the end of a horizontal wire. The shape of the weight ensures that the increased buoyancy compensates for the (average) diminution in cross section (Andrade 1910). The other method, of which at least two variants have been proposed, involves systems of levers (Caffyn 1944 and Andrade 1948).

Creep generally proceeds in three fairly distinct stages. Initially there is a decelerating flow, as the sample hardens. This is often known as *primary creep*. It is followed by a region of constant rate of flow known as *secondary creep* and finally, by a third stage in which there is acceleration, known as *tertiary creep*. Some rheologists have preferred to classify creep in terms of whether the deformation is recoverable or not, when the load is removed. The objection to this distinction is that recovery is sometimes so slow that it is hard to know when it is complete. The creep of metals will be discussed by Mr Graham in Appendix 1.

The extension of strips of material is also quite widely used but the theory is

---

* Sinusoidal tests are also done, from which a "creep compliance" may be calculated. We are not here concerned with this (see Chapter 7).

very complex. For theoretical studies, Weissenberg (1949) has stretched strips of cloth and studied the shape of cuts made in the strip. The strips could be constrained in various ways and the effects on the stress in different parts of the sample are seen from the distortions of the cuts.

For some reason, very little work has been done on the compression of cylinders whose height is considerably greater than the diameter. Many years ago, I showed that, if cylinders of a bitumen, shown by other methods to be very nearly Newtonian, are compressed in this way and compensation is made for change in cross-section, good straight lines are obtained when the rate of change of strains (Hencky's formula) are plotted against the compressive stresses. W. Lethersich pointed out that, for Newtonian fluids, the extension of a rod under constant *load* (or compression of a cylinder) gives a constant rate of change of strain if a rather unusual formula is used for the strain: $(l — l_0)/l$, where l_0 is the original, and l the strained length of the test-piece.

For some reason, most rheologists have preferred to compress disks, for which the situation is much more complicated. Following early calculations (in 1874) by J. Stefan, R. L. Peek and J. R. Scott have derived equations for the compression of disks. A good modern version of the treatment, which is too complex to be discussed here, is given by Gent (1960). (The equation includes the fifth power of the height of the disk.)

For flour-doughs, a useful method was developed by P. Halton, in which two prongs were pushed into the middle of a very carefully prepared sphere of dough and then drawn apart so that the dough formed a continuous band. Measurements of the stretching of this band* gave information more in line with the judgments of bakers than did data from extending cylinders on a bath of mercury. This was probably because the sphere could be prepared much more gently than the cylinder. To form the latter, the dough had to be forced out of a short narrow tube. The same criticism might be levelled at the method that Schofield and I used in which cylinders of dough were suspended and extended under their own weight. A scale had been impressed in wet enamel on the undeformed cylinder and, after a given time, the cylinder was carefully laid in a horizontal position, and the now distorted scale was printed off onto suitable paper. The stresses and strains were calculated at points along the scale. The method is quite a useful one for materials which can be got into cylindrical form without destroying their structure.

Two other methods have been widely used for testing flour-doughs. The first, invented by M. Chopin, consists in blowing a bubble in a disk of dough and measuring the internal pressure and the size of the bubble. This is clearly

---

* The method is also used for testing rubber bands.

H

imitative of the action of yeast, and should measure the capacity of a dough to withstand such pressures. Many years ago, work which I published with my late French colleague, P. Potel, seemed to show no clear correlation between the Chopin parameters and the quality of the dough as judged by bakers and millers. But, since the method is I believe still in use, perhaps the population of flours that was studied was not typical.

Another type of instrument originally called a *Farinograph*, invented by C. W. Brabender, originally in Germany, has a wider application and has been used not only for doughs but for many other materials. In the case of dough, the flour and water are mixed in a specially constructed mixer which works at constant speed and the energy needed to maintain the mixing is recorded. Naturally, this energy at first increases until the dough is fully formed. Later, however, the structure breaks down at a rate which is a function of the "strength" (i.e. capacity to make a good large loaf) of the dough. Care must be taken that the dough (or other material) does not stick to the blades of the mixer; otherwise part of the energy measured is that needed to tear the dough from the blades and not to mould it.

Another popular empirical method used for soap, butter, cheese and other materials is to measure the force required to cut through a block of the material with a standard wire. The instrument for doing this is called a *sectilometer*. It does not measure any well-defined physical property but is imitative of the way in which many of these materials are cut into blocks, in practice. Indeed it is almost impossible to cut through an ordinary Cheddar cheese with a saw!

Penetrometers have been used for cheese* of much the same type as the loaded needle penetrometer for bitumen testing. There is one big difference, however. Bitumen is fairly homogeneous and a single needle is all that is needed: cheese has small holes, tough and soft spots, etc., and even the use of three needles simultaneously has not proved altogether satisfactory.

We have discussed hardness in an earlier chapter. Indentation tests are widely used, not only for metals. Cones and spheres are the most usual indenting bodies and sometimes the elastic recovery, after removal of load, is measured as well as the depth of depression under load. A study of the distribution of strains around the indenting body is quite complicated.

A few materials can be compressed in bulk and I used this method many years ago to try to measure what the farmer calls the "tilth" of his soil, i.e.

---

* The reader may wonder why the rheological properties of cheese should be important, within wide limits. This has little to do with spreading or chewing. The point is that the consistency of a young cheese greatly influences the types of micro-organism that can grow in it and hence its eventual flavour and smell.

its capacity to make a good seed-bed. The farmer often judges this by the reaction of the soil to his foot; but the farmer's foot is sometimes too small to test a fair sample or is even occasionally smaller than the biggest individual lumps of soil. Experiments were carried out in the middle thirties at the Rothamsted Experimental Station in which big heavy metal cylinders were lowered, by means of a winch, onto soil prepared in various ways. Creep and recovery curves were obtained in this way and showed considerable hysteresis. However, the work was left unfinished and no attempt was made adequately to study the farmer as distinct from the soil.

Resilience is generally measured in terms of the height of re-bound of a metal sphere dropped onto the sample. The ratio of height of rebound to that of the height from which the sphere was dropped, is sometimes called the *restitution coefficient*. The term "Resiliency" is sometimes used to denote springiness, or something very like it. This method can be used, of course, only when there is a marked difference between the measured resilience and that of the metal sphere. For very soft materials, a ball may be rolled down a slope and bounced on the surface to be tested. Bouncing off the surface, the ball falls onto a thin sheet of paper below which is a carbon-paper. This leaves a "dot" at the point where the ball fell and its distance from the point of impact can be measured.

The bending of strips and torsion of rods are more the concern of the engineer than of the rheologist. Nevertheless such methods are sometimes used to measure the elastic properties of solid materials. When a rod is twisted, there are changes in length which may be either increased or decreased. The causes of these effects are quite complex and are fully discussed in M. Reiner's book "Deformation, Strain and Flow" (see Appendix 3). Tension and torsion are also often applied simultaneously.

Another method which concerns the engineer is what is called *triaxial stressing* and this has been considerably used for work on soils and rocks. A cylinder of material is subjected to axial compression and at the same time, to an isotropic pressure in the perpendicular directions. This method is used to measure conditions of fracture.

In some cases, especially with biological materials, there has been confusion between the yield-stress, needed to start a material flowing, and the rupture stress, at which the structure is irreversibly broken down. Theories of fracture are too complex to come within the scope of this book: suffice it to say that there has been much argument as to which property is critical. Is it a strain, a stress or an energy? The story is well told in J. C. Jaeger's book "Elasticity, Fracture and Flow" (see Appendix 3). "Strength of Materials" really forms a separate discipline but it is clearly closely linked to rheology.

We have already mentioned the practical difficulty in distinguishing very slow recovery of some materials from permanent "set". As M. Reiner has pointed out in his "Deformation, Strain and Flow", permanent set is often due to the filling up of pores and holes in the material (e.g. concrete, cheese). With solid bodies, the presence of sharp depressions on the surface ("notches") will cause a concentration of stresses which will often weaken the whole sample.

One further property of certain solids, such as some paints and soils, which should be mentioned is called *crazing*. This refers to the formation of large cracks in the material as it dries or is stretched. The latter process can be imitated by putting a layer of the material on a rubber sheet which can then be stretched in various ways. This method has been developed by K. Weissenberg and his colleagues.

16/Some Applications of Rheology

Various practical applications of rheology have already been mentioned in this book but, so far, the aim has been rather to acquaint the "non-rheologist" with the basic principles of the science. With the exception of the chapters on biorheology, little has been said about the practical uses that are being made of rheology. In this last chapter, a few of the materials for which rheology is used will be discussed, although of course the list is far from complete. Metals are dealt with separately in Appendix 1, and biological materials will not be included, since they have already been fairly fully discussed.

Nor is it possible to mention all the methods of testing, even in common use. The examples given must be taken as being no more than illustrations of some of the work that is going on. For convenience, the materials will be listed in alphabetical order. References to sources of information will not be given: they will be found in the books listed in Appendix 3.

Asphalts, Bitumens and Tars

It is clear that these materials form a group to the study of which rheology is admirably suited. Tars are liquids and generally not highly anomalous. A few bitumens are approximately true fluids (e.g. Californian bitumen) but most show elastic properties.

Asphalts are generally obtained from crude petroleum by removing the volatile components. The consistency may be further increased by the addition of other materials. Practical tests are generally of two kinds: penetrometry and "softening-point" tests. Needle penetrometers are frequently used, also the indentation of a sphere resting on the sample may be measured.

The "Ring and Ball" test (which sounds like the name of a "pub"!) is carried out by measuring the temperature at which a disk of asphalt, resting on a brass ring, deforms to a defined extent under the weight of a metal ball resting on it. Asphalts are said to differ in "type" when the temperatures corresponding to a certain penetration and that measured by the "ring and ball" differ considerably. From these tests, a "penetration index" has been defined and this is found to correlate with the extent of deviation from Newtonian behaviour. Most asphalts show measurable elasticity but quite complex "dashpot and spring" models would be needed adequately to describe their behaviour, though the Maxwell Model often gives a fair approximation.

Experiments have, naturally, been done, applying an alternating load to rods of high consistency asphalts, and the equations given in Chapter 7 have been applied. At most frequencies, the static and dynamic elastic moduli differ very little. Interesting relationships have been found between the chemical constitution of asphalts and their rheological properties.

In practice, more interest is shown in the properties of asphalts containing mineral aggregates. Many tests are in use, including sinusoidal straining and triaxial stressing. Various empirical equations have been proposed to relate consistency to the concentration of the filler: it is obvious that none of the equations discussed in earlier chapters is likely to be applicable. (The rather remarkable results of Arnstein and Reiner for certain cements have already been described.) For more solid materials, breaking strength tests are also used.

Biscuits, bread and cakes

Most of the interest in rheology as applied to biscuit manufacture has been in France. Tests have been done on the strength of biscuits; their tendency to break; but the main concern is with the doughs. Although biscuit doughs require to have different rheological properties from those of bread flour-doughs (since the dough is not required to expand much) this subject had best be dealt with under "bread-doughs". The rheology of baked bread and of cakes has aroused considerable interest, especially in connection with the complex phenomena of staling.

The chemical aspects of staling are now fairly well understood but do not concern us here. A convenient method for measuring the rheological properties is to load a small standard cylinder of bread or cake and observe its compression under load as well as its recovery after the load is removed. The load-compression curves are sigmoid in shape. An automatic parallel-plate rheometer has also been used for disk-shaped samples and a complex model with eight elements has been proposed in Britain, although Hungarian workers regard the "Burgers model", with the addition of what is virtually a "slider", as an adequate approximation.

Breaking strength and "stickiness" of cake sponges have also been measured. That the quality of bread can be predicted from rheological data obtained from the dough is generally assumed. A brief description of tests on dough has already been given in this book and there are probably several hundred papers on the subject; but there is a singular lack of quantitative comparison between the rheological data and the judgments of expert bakers and millers, or even such a rough indication of quality as loaf-volume.

(In early times, much work was done on the flow-properties of suspensions of flour but this has been entirely superseded by work on dough.)

Butter

The most important rheological characteristic of butter is the property known in the trade by the cumbersome name "spreadability". (The French have even introduced "tartinabilité"!) Many tests have been devised, especially in Wageningen (Netherlands) and at the National Institute for Research in Dairying in England, to measure this property. These include machines which actually spread the butter and measure the length of the smear under standard conditions, compression of cylinders, sectility with a wire-cutter and even bending of "beams" of butter. Tests have also been done both with large groups of housewives and with especially trained panels to find out just what is meant by good "spreadability". Doubtless the meaning may differ in different localities, some people preferring firmer butters than others; but, although many of the tests correlate highly with consumer preference, strangely enough, it seems as though the highest correlation is that with the force needed to extrude the butter at a standard rate through a standard short narrow tube. Strictly speaking, correlation coefficients should not be used for ordinal scales; nevertheless, the results are almost certainly meaningful.

It goes without saying that a careful temperature control is essential for all such tests. Other fats, margarine, etc., have been studied by similar methods.

Ceramic clays

The ceramics industry in all countries has been slow to take up rheological testing. Reference has already been made to an indirect plasticity test dependent on measuring the flow of a "slip" (paste) through a capillary. Many other tests, such as compression, bending and torsion of cylinders, have been described, and of course strength tests on fired ware are well known. But it is hard to persuade the potter (especially the art-potter) to describe in terms understandable to the rheologist, how he judges the quality of a clay. As early as the sixteenth century, Bernard Palissy in France (and doubtless others still earlier in China) knew that there are many different kinds of clays, suited to different types of ware.

Cheese

The quality of a cheese depends largely on the types of micro-organism which can develop in it and this, in turn, depends on what the cheese-maker calls "body" and the rheologist, "consistency". (The term "texture", used for most foodstuffs to include consistency, is strictly reserved in the cheese trade for what can be seen and not felt.)

Many of the usual rheological methods have been tried on cheese and on the "intermediate", curd. Sinusoidal straining in the cheese vat as the milk gradually sets to a gel has replaced earlier methods of measuring a static shear modulus, mainly because the latter was generally measured on the surface where the temperature is below that of the bulk of the material. On the finished cheese, a sphere compressor has proved useful but, for the less homogeneous brands, rather a large and correspondingly heavy load has to be applied. Heterogeneity also causes difficulties for sectilometers and needle penetrometers. Compression of cylinders has proved fairly effective if it is permitted to take samples out of the cheese.

In cheese of the Gruyère type, the shape, size and positioning of holes and cracks are certainly related to rheological properties which can sometimes be measured before the holes develop. The cracks near the corners (which the French call "lainures") form at an angle of 45° to the vertical, in the plane where the shear stresses are maximal.

Chocolate

Work has been published on the consistency of chocolate, especially at the stage of manufacture known as "conching", which involves prolonged agitation at a temperature of 40°–50°. Molten chocolate is in many ways similar to a clay paste, and all the usual methods, capillary, coaxial cylinder, falling sphere, etc., have been used. Chocolate and cocoa differ principally in their fat contents. The effects of the addition of various quantities of lecithin increases its viscosity on stirring. It is not clear to what extent this is a dilatancy and to what extent some other form of shear-thickening.

Drilling muds

These substances are used to lubricate drills in boring for oil. It is advantageous that they should be thixotropic, so that they may form a solid structure when the drill is not operating but should flow readily when stirred. In modern times, various substances are added to natural clays to get the best rheological properties. The most thixotropic of naturally occurring clays is bentonite, but this would not be suitable without modification.

Eggs

Experiments have been done, both on egg white, which consists essentially of two separate phases, and on the unbroken egg. The consistency of the contents of the latter has been measured by attaching the egg to an oscillating pendulum system and measuring the damping which is, of course, greater the more the energy absorbed in producing flow inside the egg.

Emulsions

The rheology of emulsions is so well dealt with in the two books by P. Sherman listed in Appendix 3 that nothing further will be added here.

Fish

From the rheological point of view, toughness is of prime importance and needle penetrometers are perhaps most widely used. Viscosities of fish proteins have also been measured and related to freshness, but not to toughness. If fish is broken up into a suspension, the optical density is found to be correlated with the toughness of the original sample.

Fruit and vegetables

Most of the work on these materials has been done in America but there is a wide interest also in France. Penetrometers again play a prominent part, but for green peas, an instrument called the "tenderometer" is widely used. This consists of two series of parallel plates, somewhat like a variable condenser, between which the peas are crushed. The toughness of peas is highly dependent on the age at which they are picked but of course the methods of processing are also important.

Automatic recording of the dynamic moduli of potatoes, pears, etc., has been developed in Sweden. The noise made by the jaws in chewing various foodstuffs, which, other things being equal, gives an indication of their toughness, has been measured by B. Drake, using an ingenious electronic device.

Geological systems

The flow of lava and of glaciers (ice) have been fairly widely studied. Lavas differ greatly in chemical composition. In this respect and in their rheological behaviour, they are very much like glasses. On a recent visit to Iceland, I could not find out much about their flow properties but they are doubtless approximately Newtonian at high temperatures.

In Japan, studies have been made on the propagation of sound waves through the earth's crust, in connection with earthquake research.

Glass

The changing rates of flow of glass fibres with rise in temperature have been widely studied, usually by loading a fibre hung vertically in a furnace. Glass is popularly said to be a true fluid, even at room temperature; but it is probable that this is seldom the case. The "glassy" state is sometimes considered as a fourth state of matter (as distinct from gases, liquids and solids). Normal glass is not crystalline in the ordinary sense but it contains well-defined units of structure: the silica tetrahedra. The term "glassy state", however, often refers to the condition of high polymers over a certain range of temperature. Coaxial cylinder viscometers have also been used for the study of liquid glasses.

Grease

Lubricating greases are dispersions of such materials as soaps, bentonite clay or silica gel in oils. At high shear-rates, they behave, as do most oils, as Newtonian liquids. At low stresses, they show yield-values but are seldom simple Bingham systems, since the flow curves are not straight, the greases are generally appreciably elastic and some are thixotropic. They are, in fact, among the most complex systems studied by industrial rheologists. They have been studied at high shear-rates using almost all the standard types of viscometer. In industry, a specially designed cone is allowed to fall into the grease and the depth of penetration is measured; but often, the quality of grease is judged by the "feel" (principally "tack", no doubt) of the sample between the finger and thumb of the expert.

Ink (printing)

Much rheological work has been done on printing inks, especially in relation to the mechanical measurement of "tack" and various "tackmeters" have been devised. The "fly" of ink is a curious phenomenon which is probably related to both electrical and rheological properties. Many different types of rheometer have been used.

Metals (See Appendix 1)

Meat and muscle

Meat is a difficult material for the rheologist because, although its properties, especially toughness, are quite important, its fibrous nature makes for difficulties in preparing suitable test-pieces. The principal methods of testing have been (a) an instrument similar to the "pea tenderometer", (b) penetrometers: blunt rods and wedges, (c) measurements of power needed to mince and (d) machines imitating the action of the human jaw, with dentures attached! Now that meat can be "tenderized", either by the action of chemical substances or mechanically, measures of tenderness become of increasing importance.

Milk and Cream

Milk is very nearly Newtonian but, as the butter-fat content is increased, the rheology becomes more and more complex. Even quite thick creams (up to 48% fat) can remain non-Newtonian liquids if very carefully treated after manufacture and show a double-logarithmic relation between stress and shear-rate over a wide range. But the least roughness of handling causes a clumping of the fat globules and a yield-value appears. Changes of temperature can produce almost unbelievable differences in the consistencies of creams having the same fat contents.

The viscosity of milk, and its variation with temperature and with temperature-treatments (pasteurization, etc.) have proved somewhat disappointing properties for practical purposes.

Paints, varnishes, etc.

These are among the earliest systems to be studied by rheologists. N. Casson's work on the structure of "filled" varnishes has already been mentioned. In early times, E. C. Bingham based much of his rheological theory on work on paint. Later, paint was the first material for which the sigma effect was observed. In modern paints, thixotropy and consistency play a major role.

Plastics (high polymers) and synthetic rubbers

By far the widest application of rheology to any industry has been that concerned with plastics. Since these are generally synthetic materials, a knowledge of their molecular structure is highly important, both in their finished form and in intermediate stages in their manufacture. There is a vast literature relating rheological properties to chemical constitution and structure.

An important feature has been the relationships between such properties as intrinsic viscosity and molecular weight, or distance between junction points in structural molecules. Unfortunately molecular weights have to be considered statistically, and quite a number of possible ways of "averaging" exists. Viscosity measurements are related to a somewhat unusual kind of average and indeed there is some danger that, since different physical measurements tend each to measure a particular type of average, it is difficult to check one against another or to interpret them meaningfully. In spite of all this, however, rheology has proved of great value to the industry and almost all the methods, fundamental and empirical, mentioned in this book, as well as many others, are in use. We have already briefly discussed the high-elasticity of rubber.

Soap

An important feature of soap is the way in which salts tend to diffuse through it. This affects the hardness and the process has been followed by measuring the force on a wire ("sectility") cutting through the soap. Soap solutions have also been studied by rheologists.

Soil

Work has been discussed briefly earlier in this book.

Starches

We have already discussed the "retrogradation" of starch in Chapter 9. The rheologist generally studies starch either as a paste or as a gel. There are several commercial instruments for determining the consistency of the pastes, depending on the measure of the force required to stir at a constant speed. Such methods have the disadvantage that the stirring itself produces marked effects and the results are, therefore, greatly dependent on the speed. Considerable work has been done on the effects of various electrolytes and on viscosity-concentration relations.

Starch gel-strengths are generally measured by means of penetrometers. Starches from different plant sources show very different behaviour.

Wood and paper

You will remember, from Chapter 2, that for a completely anisotropic material there are 21 independent elastic constants, and for an isotropic material, only 2. Wood is intermediate, since its properties along and across the grain are different but it has a certain degree of isotropy because of its properties in the plane at right-angles to the grain. In this respect, it resembles the rhombic crystals. Stresses and strains are resolved along the grain, across the grain and around the grain (i.e. within concentric circles) and the elastic properties may be described in terms of 12 constants: 3 Young's moduli, 3 shear moduli and 6 Poisson's ratios. However, these are interrelated by simple equations and there are only 9 independent constants.

One of the most important properties of wood is its swelling in water and the effects of swelling on the elastic constants have been studied. Wood also shows elastic hysteresis, i.e. it does not obey Hooke's law except for very small strains and the loading and unloading curves from a loop. With care, these loops are reproducible in some cases.

A particularly interesting material is plywood because, in this, layers of wood are glued together in such a way that the grain of one layer may be at right-angles to that of its neighbour and the glue junction may be stronger than the wood. The elastic properties of such systems are very complex.

Most modern paper is made from wood fibres. These are laid down with such an orientation that the paper has properties somewhat like those of a handkerchief (though not so marked) which cannot be stretched easily on a "normal" pull, but will shear quite a long way if pulled from opposite corners. It is hardly surprising that Sweden has taken the lead in studying the rheology of paper.

Wet and dry strength are generally measured by means of a pendulum breaker; bursting tests under air-pressure are also used. Paper is by no means Hookean. It shows delayed elasticity, permanent "set" and stress relaxation. Its properties also differ in what are called the "machine" and the "cross" directions, i.e. depending on the orientation of the fibres. The "creep" curves for paper are comparable to those of certain metals. Dashpot spring models have been proposed but these can only approximate to the real behaviour of paper. Eyring's theory of rate-processes (see Chapter 3) has been applied to explain the rheological behaviour of paper.

Appendices

Appendix 1
Rheology of Metals
by A. Graham

Not many people who work with metals—if they have heard of rheology which is not always the case—would accept that rheology relates to metals. Their view is matched by the fact that rheologists find little of interest in books concerned with metals. The situation reaffirms the theme of the first chapter that agreement needs to be reached upon terminology; upon the meanings and uses of technical terms; upon what is meant by "rheology". Metals form the class of materials longest to have received the attentions of modern technology and science. The problems of metals draw attention to features of inanimate nature, and of human judgment also, which bear upon the question.

The view of rheology taken by metallurgists, metal-physicists, metallurgical engineers and their kind derives from craft traditions according to which materials have been classified—metals, wood, clay, rubber, foodstuffs, and so on—by their self-evident differences. The classification has led to the growth of distinct and sophisticated disciplines, each closely associated with a single class of material. Thus "metallurgy", "rubber technology", "glass technology", "polymer physics", etc. It may appear at first from the viewpoint of any one of these branches that rheology relates only to "odd" materials, to studies of the mechanical behaviours of mud, printers' ink, biological materials, etc. which, in contrast with metals for example, are orphan children of dubious legitimacy having little or no standing in the respectable world of organized knowledge.

Craft terminologies are based of course upon a different organization of knowledge from that which is the aim of exact science. Exact science certainly aims to identify distinct phenomena; also to define the precise conditions that need to be fulfilled if each identified phenomenon is to be produced, reproduced and ultimately controlled at will. However, it also studies phenomena with a view to identifying simple common factors which link together as many diverse phenomena as may prove to be possible. For example, progress made with exact studies of rubbers, glass and polymers has already bridged some of the superficial differences between them. Polymers have been found to take rubber-like and glass-like forms as limiting cases, and all three are now being linked to some extent by the theory of *elastomers*. Scientific knowledge is largely organized on the basis of common factors; and, as progress is made, a new terminology develops, one that rests upon essential rather than superficial differences.

The definition of "rheology" by common consent in Chapter 1 refers the term to both the mechanical properties and constitution of matter. The definition creates an immediate difficulty of distinguishing rheological studies from studies which, by the common consent of other groups of people than rheologists, form distinct disciplines like those previously mentioned. Of these, metallurgy is a firm example. Following upon the extensive development of techniques for observation of the internal structures of metals with optical and electron microscopes, the constitution of metals has become one of the essential provinces of metallurgy, especially physical metallurgy. Moreover, metallurgy shares with mechanical engineering an interest in machines and structures made from metals. In the association, they are jointly concerned with the close dependence of the mechanical performance of metals upon their compositions and internal structures. Thus metallurgy and engineering share out between them in respect of metals the constitution and mechanical-property interests of rheology. Constitution forms the central interest of metallurgy, with mechanical properties as such in detail a somewhat secondary interest. The emphasis in engineering is reversed. However, the definition of rheology makes no distinctions of emphasis.

Engineering interests overlap with those of rheology in another respect, also namely in the problem of "a lump of material acted upon by forces in any direction and strained in any direction" (Chapter 2). Engineering interests are treated in a formal manner in the sophisticated discipline of *stress analysis*. This links both with "applied mechanics". The classical theories of elasticity and hydrodynamics supply a foundation for the reasoning. The exclusion from rheology by common consent of the theories of elasticity and hydrodynamics, if taken literally, has the consequence of excluding simpler aspects of the "lump of material" problem in favour of more complex aspects. Neither for engineering nor for rheology are the classical theories as they stand acceptable. A lump of metal, as of any other material, behaves neither as a perfectly elastic solid nor as a perfect fluid, but, according to circumstances, displays some proportion of the features of both. The blade of a working steam turbine may vibrate and emit a note like an elastic tuning fork; while over years of service will gradually "creep", or flow. The balance between elastic and creep or inelastic deformation depends upon the constitution and temperature of the material, distribution of forces over the material, rate of application of the forces, period the forces remain applied; also their manner of variation if they vary. The classical theories over-simplify the situation and need to be adapted and extended.

Any theory, whether classical, or rheological, will be concerned, whatever the material, with three distinct aspects. They are, firstly, that of the relative positions and relative motions of each small element of the lump with respect to the other elements; secondly, that of the balance of forces between each element and its immediate neighbours; and thirdly that of the dependence of the forces exerted by any element upon the shape, size and changes of shape and size, of the element. If either the material is devoid of structure or its structure is disregarded, the first aspect is a matter of account-keeping irrespective (in principle) of the nature of the material. Moreover, since the laws of statics and dynamics are taken to be the same for all materials, and the same within a deforming material as between material and material regarded as rigid bodies, the second aspect similarly is not concerned (in principle) with the nature of the material. These aspects offer means for distinguishing rheological from other treatments only by the fact that general statements involve such heavy mathematics that simplifying approximations which recognize no more than extreme features of special classes of materials seem to be essential. Some of the approximations appear to be claimed by rheology, others by other disciplines. The approximations of the classical theories are, for elastic solids, very small deformations and for hydro-dynamical fluids, that the amount of deformation is irrelevant. As particular cases they include a state of rest, of accelerated motion only, of steady motion only. They represent ideal situations to which materials of different classes may conform in certain circumstances. Rheological treatments of highly-elastic materials which, after large deformations, recover shape and size when loads are removed, favour different approximations from those favoured for treatment of the inelastic or plastic deformation of metals. For the latter, the classical equations are retained except that deformation is assumed to take place at constant volume. With materials of rheological interest, K. Weissenberg has drawn attention to the importance of the energy associated with a change of volume. It is an open question, however, whether such differences of treatment should exclude metals from the province of rheology.

Comments are similar in respect of the third aspect, namely that of the relationship of the forces exerted by an element of material to its configuration and change of configuration. All treatments are governed by approximation. Different approximations are suggested by the peculiarities of distinct groups of materials. It is an open question whether "rheology" is confined to certain groups.

A consideration that dominates the third aspect is the variety of materials and complexity of their constitutions. Rheological approaches to these matters may be set alongside the fact that, with metals, two quite distinct approaches are followed with rather slender liaison between them. One is the approach of engineering and stress analysis which demands mathematical relationships between the components (in different spatial directions) of stress and deformation or rate of deformation. The other is the approach of metallurgy and metal-physics which demands that the component forces and deformations shall be related to the constitution and internal structure of a metal. In practice, stress analysis faces such mathematical complication that the relationships are chosen as much for convenience as for being precise statements of physical behaviour. In metal-physics, the complexities of structure are such that the possibility of relating behaviour to structure are regarded as being confined to such small ranges of stress, strain, temperature, and either of time or rate of straining, that only one structural mechanism out of many possible mechanisms will be acting. Because of the difficulty of mutual interactions between different mechanisms, it appears true to write that all treatments of the third aspect in terms of a detailed structural model of the material embody the last assumption. Statistical treatments of structure, such as those of the theory of high-elasticity, are not immune from this comment.

The division between the two types of approach runs close to that which separates the pragmatical approach of engineering from the ideals of pure science. The success of pure science in relating human-scale events to events on microscopic and smaller scales of observation has led almost to an identification of pure science with study of those relationships. Related divisions of interest run right through the field of the mechanical behaviour of materials irrespective of the naming of any particular area. Interest is largely divided between the bases of mechanical behaviour with constitution as the primary interest, the demands of stress analysis for tractable mathematical expressions although these may be physically untenable, and the demands for engineering for particular materials with adequate mechanical properties for some particular purpose. Scant interest is taken in mechanical properties, as such, as a worthy study in its own right. Mechanical properties are like the Cinderella who is called upon to do all the work but is not invited to the party.

If other disciplines are interested in structure and applications with some reference to mechanical properties, it would not seem inappropriate for rheology to be interested in mechanical properties with some reference to applications and structure. The present Appendix is concerned with the possibility that in these circumstances no distinctions need be drawn which would maintain a barrier between metals and materials of rheological interest. It is concerned with a lengthy study of metals based upon a close similarity between the mechanical behaviour of metals, as represented by certain experimentally-based formulae in engineering, and the behaviour of a variety of rheological materials, as represented by an equation due to Nutting and the author of this book.

Metals, like other self-supporting solids, have the experimental advantage that the dependence of the forces upon the shape, size, and changes of shape and size, of an element are amenable to measurement upon a rod of uniform section loaded in the direction of its length. In a uniaxial specimen of this kind, only the normal components of stress and strain along the axis of the rod are of immediate interest, and each has a common single magnitude (while the deformation remains stable) in all elements of the rod. A presumption embodied in theories of the compound loading of metals is that the elastic and inelastic behaviour of an element under these simple conditions of loading is typical of its behaviour in general. The presumption incorporates others, namely, that deformation comprises the simple sum of an elastic and an inelastic component, and that application of a uniform hydrostatic pressure with associated change of volume has no influence on the latter. The inelastic deformation of an element under any state of stress may then be deduced from the uniaxial results, because one state of stress may be changed to another by application, in principle, of the appropriate pressure. Experiments with uniaxial stress clearly show that the relation of inelastic strain to stress is strongly dependent upon temperature, and also in general upon time: the observed strain depends on the rate of application of the stress; it also increases with time if the stress remains constant. In these circumstances, the problem of the third aspect thus reduces to a study of the relationship between stress, inelastic strain, time, and temperature, in a uniaxial specimen. For consistency with the references quoted below, these quantities will be symbolized respectively by σ, ε, t and T.

The literature contains results of uniaxial experiments performed on a great variety of metals, especially under conditions of constant stress (creep tests), progressively increasing stress (tensile tests), and periodic tests (fatigue tests). In most instances, temperature is held constant during any one experiment, and may be held at a succession of constant values in different experiments. Many considerations determine the selection of results of interest. Individual authors have put forward different formulae, whether purely "empirical" to express their results, or based on some physical consideration. The legitimate aims of both engineering and metal physics, the one to express common features of behaviour for use in stress calculations, the other to relate differences of behaviour to differences of structure, are in evident contrast. Present interest is in the marked similarity between the forms of curve which result when quite different metals are subjected to the same kind of test, e.g. when creep results are compared with creep results, tensile with tensile, etc. Creep tests are the simplest because stress and temperature then both remain constant. The mathematical forms of curve resulting from creep tests on high-purity lead, tin, cadmium (Andrade, 1910, 1914), aluminium and other metals are not easily distinguished, except for magnitudes of constants, from those of similar tests performed on complex steels, for example a nickel chromium steel hardened with additions of carbon, aluminium and titanium. The forms are not of course identical: if they were, the rheology of metals would be an established discipline. Much depends upon the attitude adopted towards differences.

For purposes of stress analysis and engineering, it has been supposed that, with metals of practical interest, stress, strain, time and temperature are related, by analogy with the relation

$$pv = RT$$

for gases, by some algebraic equation. The supposition appears to have been initiated by Ludwick (1909) and extended and applied by Bailey (1932, 1935) and many others also. Hollomon (1947) appears to have been the first to have advanced a complete expression. He supposed that t entered only in combination with ε as the derivative $d\varepsilon/dt$ or $\dot{\varepsilon}$; he then assembled experimental evidence relating to a number of steels and other metals in support of an algebraic relationship between σ, ε, $\dot{\varepsilon}$ and T. Agreement, although encouraging, was not exact; however, exact results are not the rule in science.

Analogous reasoning may be shown to lead to a similar but rather simpler equation, namely

$$\frac{\sigma}{\sigma_r} = \left(\frac{\varepsilon}{\varepsilon_r}\right)^{\mu T} \left(\frac{\dot{\varepsilon}}{\dot{\varepsilon}_r}\right)^{pT/T}$$

in which μ, p and the symbols with subscripts r are constants. It has the virtue of combining into a single expression 14 different equations which were set up to represent complementary results of their various experiments by Ludwick (1909), Bailey (1932), Soderberg (1936), Zener and Hollomon (1944), MacGregor and Fisher (1945) and others. The several equations represent various aspects of the relationship between the several variables, as observed in various types of experiment on various metals. Apart from insignificant differences in respect of temperature, the Hollomon equation is a special case. Of interest to rheology is the fact that, when T is constant, this experimental equation for metals becomes the same as the likewise experimental equation

$$\varepsilon = \psi\sigma^{\beta}t^{k},$$

in which ψ, β and k are constants. It was first put forward by Nutting (1921) to describe his experimental results on pitch, and then supported later by the extensive researches of Scott Blair (1949). They showed it satisfactorily fitted experimental results of various kinds performed on non-metals ranging from elastic solids to viscous fluids, and from pitch to flour-dough and cheese. In view of this experimental evidence for a quantitative similarity of behaviour over a wide variety of materials, the standing of these equations appears to be of no small importance to rheology. The objection they face is that they do not have the form of relationships that are usually derived by applications of familiar principles in physics to a representative model of a material.

The criteria of validity in terms of which this evidence of coordination should be judged include, as with any kind of relationship between experimental quantities, the exactness of fitting relative to the number of physical factors which may influence results. The implications of this criterion are not always recognized. In the case of metals, if not of other materials also, the questions of exactness of fitting and of number of factors present appear to be inextricably tied together in a Gordian knot. Experiment clearly shows:

(i) that different specimens of nominally the same metal may differ considerably in performance, and consequently that regular trends can only be firmly established if the experimental range is sufficient in relation to the scatter. Extensions of the range however lead to the difficulty that factors not taken into account may disturb the results. Metallurgical studies clearly show further that:

(ii) complex structural processes accompany deformation on all scales of magnitude down to the scale of atoms;

(iii) many such processes usually occur simultaneously.

Thus, although one process may be contrived in some way to predominate over a restricted range of experiment, any extension of the range may allow other processes to have an influence. The full significance of an experimental trend, which is presumed to derive from one predominating process, cannot therefore be assessed without firm knowledge of effects of the other processes. Moreover, each process to be considered is in a similar situation in this respect. Accordingly, in the absence of prior knowledge of how each individual factor can be totally isolated for detailed study, some unknown degree of approximation must inevitably be accepted. The situation outlined is not of course unique to a rheology of metals. The history of science shows that progress with many complex problems is made by a process of successively improving approximation in which postulates of separation are first tentatively made, then tested experimentally, and subsequently modified if they are not in accordance with the results.

With regard to the second criterion of validity, namely that a relationship must be "understood" in terms of familiar principles and a model, the view that the criterion may initially be discarded appears sufficiently justified by the well-known remark of Oliver Heaviside, "must I understand the process of digestion before I may eat my dinner?"

Evidently, in view of these considerations, no *a priori* proof in advance can be expected that the Nutting–Scott Blair equation is a true expression of a common rheology of metals and non-metals. The results outlined offer a choice between adopting that equation as a postulate for trial and modification, or of leaving the scientific study of metals undisturbed in the structural and constitutional provinces of metallurgy and metal physics. The first choice appears to offer means for making progress.

According to either form of the equation, if T is constant, a graph of log σ against log t with ε constant should be a straight line having a negative slope equal to the ratio k/β of the Nutting–Scott Blair exponents. While this prediction appeared to be significantly fulfilled in the original work of these authors, a curvilinear relationship is found more generally. Of particular interest therefore is the experimental observation that the graphs obtained with a number of metals in identifiable circumstances appear to comprise two or three such linear segments with sharply-curved, possibly even sharp, transitions between them (Grant and Bucklin 1950). The feature is open to the interpretation that each segment is contributed by a different structural process. The question whether such processes should be presumed to occur separately in turn, or simultaneously with rapid changes in relative importance, was open to investigation. Experiment favoured the second possibility (Graham 1960). Transitions of different degrees of sharpness, as observed, could then be accommodated. Because of the situation previously mentioned, precise study of the effects of single processes in isolation appeared to be impracticable. The only alternative appeared to be to accept all processes for study simultaneously, to try out the propositions, firstly, that all obeyed the Nutting–Scott Blair equation (with different values of its constants), and secondly, that the strains each produced were additive.

Temperature is a factor of considerable significance to metals. Metals may be used over considerable ranges of temperature; their strengths or rates of deformation under a given stress vary rapidly in general with temperature;

the form and amount of variation are equally of theoretical and practical interest. To a first approximation, if a relation between σ, ε and t is measured, at a given T, in a particular kind of experiment, the effect of an increase of T is to leave the relation unchanged except that the time scale is reduced. The effect is commonly employed for the purpose of predicting from the results of short-time experiments at a higher temperature the performance of a steel loaded for long times at a lower temperature. Following a suggestion by Zener and Hollomon (1944) that, when σ and ε are constant,

$$\dot{\varepsilon}e^{-Q/RT} = \text{constant}$$

in which Q may be constant and R is the gas constant, many formal expressions for the change of time scale with T have been suggested. Their value is limited by the certain fact of metallurgical observation that different processes in metals are accelerated to different extents by increase of T. For this reason, and because of the considerations indicated above, the relative merits of different expressions are difficult to evaluate with precision. However, any one of them offers means for obtaining information to some degree of approximation concerning the σ, ε, t relationship over much wider ranges of time than would be practicable from experiments at a single temperature.

When the nearly linear segments shown by graphs of engineering test data for each of seven complex heat-resistant steels were examined from this viewpoint, the striking fact emerged (Graham 1957, Graham and Walles 1963) that the experimental points which delineated corresponding segments for different steels did not reliably distinguish differences of slope between the steels. Moreover, the mean slopes of the segments in succession indicated that the successive ratios k/β took values close to the regular sequence of fractions $\frac{1}{4}$, $\frac{1}{8}$, $\frac{1}{16}$, $\frac{1}{32}$. The data related to both creep tests and fatigue tests at elevated temperature; also the complex compositions of the steels were very different. This unsolicited result thus strikingly supported the previous indication that, to a first approximation at least, the Nutting–Scott Blair equation held irrespective of the nature of the material. An association of simple common fractions with materials, like the steels, of diverse and complex compositions can only arise if the behaviour in question is governed, not by detailed features of the microstructures which distinguish one material from another, but by averages which suppress these details. The macroscopic magnitudes of interest relate of course to averages of enormous numbers of atoms. By this attempt to take all processes into account together rather than to separate and isolate them for separate study, the Gordian knot may perhaps have been cut.

With evidence, from the forms of creep curves, for an analogous relationship between strain and time irrespective of the nature of the material (Graham 1960), the conclusion suggested itself that the strain comprised the sum of a series of Nutting–Scott Blair terms:

$$\varepsilon = \sum_{\beta,\,k} \sigma^{\beta} t^{k}$$

in which the C depend upon temperature, the k take values only from the sequence 3^{n}, and the β/k only from the sequence 2^{m}, in which n and m are integers, including zero.

These regularities were indicated by a combination of results from experiments with steady loading and periodic loading. The indicated equation needs however to be reconciled with an overriding objection that has been raised to the existence of any kind of algebraic relationship whatsoever between the experimental quantities considered. Orowan (1947), Dorn (1956) and others have pointed out that, irrespective of the form of such relationship, the assumption involves a general principle which may be directly checked by experiment. Thus if, in some experiment on a specimen, it were to be arranged that σ, ε and T had given values, an algebraic relationship of the kind advocated for example by J. H. Hollomon, as mentioned above, would specify that $\dot{\varepsilon}$ had a given value. Accordingly, if it were then arranged in an experiment of a different kind on a duplicate specimen that σ, ε and T again simultaneously reached the given values, it should be found that $\dot{\varepsilon}$ again reached its given value also. With their associates, these authors performed various experiments of this nature on a number of metals, and obtained conclusive evidence that, in general, $\dot{\varepsilon}$ did not achieve its given value irrespective of the kind of experiment. The conclusion was consistent with common experience that metals deform to different extents, and have different strengths, according as the loading is steady, progressive, or periodic. Dorn in particular showed that the internal structure, constitution, or "state" changed progressively during the course of an experiment according to the manner, in detail, in which loading varied and temperature varied. With well-developed materials used in some of the circumstances which occur in engineering, departures from the assumption of an "equation of state for metals" are small enough to be disregarded, but this is not the case when effects are compared of steady and periodic loading. The objection has been shown to persist when $\dot{\varepsilon}$ is replaced by t, as in the Nutting–Scott Blair equation.

In physical science, algebraic relationships between experimental magnitudes tend, when the ranges of the magnitudes are other than infinitesimal, to be found only in special circumstances. Most relationships of this kind relate only to small increments of magnitudes of interest. When σ, ε, t relationships are studied from this point of view, experiments on metals at constant temperature are found to show that if during the progress of an experiment the stress is increased by a small amount, an incremental creep curve becomes added to the previously developing curve of strain. Any progressive increase of stress may presumably be regarded as a succession of stress increments which are added in appropriate amounts at appropriate intervals. For any variation of stress with time, the corresponding variation of strain with time should therefore be obtainable by summing the associated incremental curves of creep. It may be shown theoretically that a whole class of assumptions on these lines lead to the same conclusion, namely that, except for unspecified differences in the values of the constants C, the form of the σ, ε, t relation should be the same for constant loading as for any one specified type of progressive loading or periodic loading. The objection would still remain that the σ, ε, t relation would not be valid, as a strict equation of state, for the purpose of predicting the results of any one type of experiment from any other. However, the significance of the result stated is that, by demonstrating (with some support from experiment) that specific circumstances are conceivable in which the same values of exponents could be found with different paths of loading, the regular sequence of terms and exponents previously described is not to be set aside on the general grounds that an algebraic equation of state is invalid. With this support, the last equation is found to lead to useful comparisons between the *shapes* of curves obtained in different kinds of experiment, questions of relative scales of magnitude being deferred for later study. Incremental experiments on fully-developed steels and alloys in their safe working ranges suggest that relative scales of magnitude are determined by other factors which, in the circumstances considered, are of the second order of small quantities.

Some further considerations are conveniently brought forward in a concluding summary. The question of whether a rheology of metals may be recognized which is distinct from existing disciplines like metallurgy, stress analysis and mechanical engineering, appears to rest upon the possibility that common features of the mechanical properties of dissimilar and diverse materials, including metals, may be recognized which are sufficiently specific to form the basis of a systematic argument. Because of the number of materials which exist and variety of features which even a single one of them offers to observation, it is a question quite impracticable to settle either by *a priori* argument or by passive and unprejudiced examination of the direct results of experiment. Indeed, how the volume of results needed could even be presented for discussion is debatable. Any agreement between materials which might be demonstrated over limited experimental ranges would leave the general proposition open to question on grounds of the inevitably personal selection of ranges and materials. No direct experimental data are for this reason here presented. A general principle can only be demonstrated, to some degree of certainty, *a posteriori*. Thus, if one is prepared to adopt a principle as a postulate, it can be checked against a particular material and condition chosen at random. It remains valid if confirmed to within experimental uncertainty. Similar validation for different conditions chosen at random can eventually lead to virtual certainty. Investigations guided by these principles are in progress (Graham 1967, Walles and Tilly 1967). An early random result of interest is the support provided for the regularities indicated for metals by the experiments of Landau (1959) on milk gel. Of particular significance to postulates concerning the detailed structures of metals is the fact that, when the simplest data, namely that obtained for the condition of constant stress and temperature, for 99·995% pure aluminium are compared with similar data for complex steels—most of which derive a superior strength from the presence of dispersions of very hard constituents which are not metals but non-metals—no first-order differences in the forms of the families of curves are evident.

A final point of principle remains to be mentioned. The proposed first-order equation, whether adopted as a single term with decimal exponents as used by Nutting and Scott Blair, or as a sum of a small number of such terms with regular fractions for exponents as suggested by the evidence here summarized, is of a different kind from formulae usually provided by physical arguments. (Some exceptions, e.g. in the kinetic theory of gases, may be noted.) Physical arguments usually lead to formulae that involve the 'special functions' of mathematical physics. These consist of sums of infinite numbers of power terms having regular sequences of integers for exponents with magnitudes that extend to infinity. Not to any single term, except perhaps to terms having 0, 1, 2, 3, or somewhat larger integers for exponents, is attributed other than an approximate physical meaning. The situation arises because of the assumption of continuity and consequent use of a mathematics of continuous variables. Metals, if not also other materials, have discontinuous structures. The important question thus presents itself of the legitimacy of various procedures for assigning numbers, via experimental observations, to phenomena in nature. It is a general question which appears amenable to rational analysis.

In conclusion, Dr Scott Blair points out a feature of metals which appears to distinguish them from most of the other materials studied by rheologists. It is the extremely wide ranges of times, temperatures, deformations and loadings which are accessible to experiment without intervention of chemical changes which completely alter a material's character. The feature offers means for resolving questions which arise from the often rather small experimental differences which exist between theoretical expressions specially designed to represent limited results, expressions which may rest upon very different hypotheses.

Appendix 2
Derivation of the Poiseuille–Hagen, Margules and Stokes Equations: Some other Equations

1/The Poiseuille–Hagen equation

Consider the streamline flow of a Newtonian liquid through a capillary tube length L, radius R under a pressure difference P. At a distance r from the centre, the rate of change of velocity (v) with r will be dv/dr. This is called the "velocity gradient". In the case of capillary flow, it is the same as the rate of change of the angle of shear with time, which we have written as $\dot{\gamma}$ (rate of shear). Suppose that there were two immiscible liquids in the capillary with a straight line (in three dimensions, a circle) marking the boundary between them. After there had been some flow, this circle would become an elongated figure as shown in Fig. A2.1, which is in fact a paraboloid.

It is clear that, as r increases, dv/dr diminishes. When r = 0, dv/dr is maximal: when r = R (since it is assumed that there is no slip at the wall), it is zero.

The pressure-difference P acts over an area of πR^2, so that the force will be $P\pi R^2$, and, since the area of the wall of the tube is $2\pi RL$, the "stress" at the wall will be PR/2L, and at distance r, Pr/2L.

Following Newton's law, this is proportional to rate of shear, or

$$\frac{dv}{dr} = -\frac{1}{\eta} \cdot \frac{Pr}{2L}$$

where η is the viscosity.

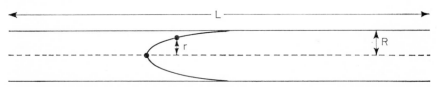

Fig. A.2.1 Streamline Flow through a Capillary

Hence $$v = -\frac{P}{2L\eta} \int r \cdot dr$$

or $$v = C - \frac{Pr^2}{4L\eta}$$

where C is an integration constant.

But when $v = 0$, $r = R$, hence $C = \dfrac{PR^2}{4L\eta}$

hence $$v = \frac{P(R^2 - r^2)}{4L\eta} \qquad (1)$$

(a) For a full capillary tube, consider the paraboloid to be made up of a series of concentric sheaths like an expanding telescope, the width of each sheath being dr. The volume of each sheath will be given by its length (v), × its circumference $2\pi r$, × its width dr. The total volume of flow per second (V) will be the integral of all these columns, from 0 to R or:

$$V = \int_0^R v \cdot 2\pi r dr$$

$$= \frac{\pi P}{2L\eta} \int_0^R (R^2 - r^2) r \cdot dr$$

$$= \frac{\pi P}{2L\eta} \left[\frac{1}{2} R^2 r^2 - \frac{1}{4} r^4 \right]_0^R$$

$$= \frac{P\pi}{8L\eta} [2R^4 - R^4]$$

$$= \frac{P\pi R^4}{8L\eta} \qquad (2)$$

This is the Poiseuille–Hagen equation.

(b) For a filling capillary, in which the length of column starts at $1 = 0$, it is clear that the flow cannot be normal close to the meniscus; but experiments which I made with coloured liquids many years ago showed that the region where the streamlines curve round is quite small and very close to the meniscus. However, because of this effect and also because of surface tension, the following treatment can be applied only when L is not very small.

Proceeding from equation (1), the maximum velocity (where $r = 0$) is

$$v_{max} = \frac{PR^2}{Vl\eta}$$

Since dv/dr varies linearly with r, the average velocity, i.e. the velocity of the whole column, must be half this. Hence

$$\frac{dl}{dt} = \frac{PR^2}{8l\eta}$$

integrating: $t = \dfrac{4\eta}{PR^2} l^2 + C'$ (C' is the integration constant.)

When $t = 0, 1 = 0$: hence $C' = 0$, or

$$\eta = \frac{t}{l^2} \cdot \frac{PR^2}{4} \tag{3}$$

(c) For an emptying capillary, the treatment is the same, except for a change of sign and a finite integration constant C''.

$$t = C'' - \frac{4\eta}{PR^2} l^2$$

when $t = 0, 1 = l_0$, i.e. the value of 1 at the start of the experiment.

Hence $$C'' = \frac{4\eta}{PR^2} l_0^2$$

and $$\eta = \frac{t}{l_0^2 - l^2} \cdot \frac{PR^2}{4} \tag{4}$$

2/The Margules equation*

The apparatus consists of a cylinder radius R_1, suspended on a torsion wire within a Newtonian liquid contained in a slightly larger cylinder, radius R_2. The height of the inner cylinder is h. (In some instruments, the inner cylinder dips only partially into the liquid, so that h may be varied but this will not be considered here.)

The outer cylinder is rotated at a constant speed of Ω rad/sec. and the torque (M) on the wire is measured. The angular velocity of the liquid at a distance r from the axis is ω. At this point let the shear stress be τ_r and the shear rate $\dot\gamma_r$.

The measured torque M is that acting on the inner surface. Between the inner cylinder and the position r, the torque exerted by the outer layers of liquid will be $\tau \times$ surface area $\times$ radius or $2\pi r^2 h \tau_r$ and, at equilibrium, this must equal τ, or:

$$\tau_r = \frac{M}{2\pi r^2 h}$$

* This treatment is taken mainly from Dinsdale and Moore's book—see Appendix 3.

To find $\dot{\gamma}$, we differentiate the linear velocity (v) (which is equal to $r\omega$) with respect to r. Hence

$$\frac{dv}{dr} = r\frac{d\omega}{dr} + \omega$$

The term ω is the radial velocity gradient of the rotating body* and, therefore, does not form part of the shear-rate, which is, therefore, in this system *not* the same as the velocity gradient.

Hence
$$\dot{\gamma}_r = r\frac{d\omega}{dr}$$

which, for a Newtonian liquid, is equal to τ_r/η.

Hence
$$\frac{d\omega}{dr} = \frac{M}{2\pi\eta hr^3}$$

Hence
$$\omega = \frac{M}{4\pi\eta hr^2} + C$$

where C is the integration constant.

Also,
$$\Omega = \frac{M}{4\pi\eta hR_2{}^2} + C$$

where Ω is ω when $r = R_2$

But, when $\omega = 0$, $r = R_1$,

hence
$$C = -\frac{M}{4\pi\eta hR_1{}^2}$$

or
$$\Omega = \frac{M(R_2{}^2 - R_1{}^2)}{4\pi\eta hR_1{}^2R_2{}^2}$$

or
$$\eta = KM\Omega$$

where K is a constant of the apparatus.

3/The Stokes equation

Note. This is found by the method of dimensions, and the numerical constant (which is, in fact, 2/9) cannot be calculated without much more complex mathematics.

---

* Imagine a rotating solid disk in which there is, of course, no shear. Suppose a point distant Δr from the centre to move through a radial distant Δl in time Δt. The velocity will be $\Delta l/\Delta t$ and the velocity gradient, $\Delta l/\Delta t\Delta r$. The angle through which the point moves is $\Delta l/\Delta r$ and the angular velocity, $\omega = \Delta l/\Delta r.\Delta t$. Hence there is a velocity gradient equal to the angular velocity, quite apart from any shearing.

We *assume* that the rate of fall (v) of a sphere in a large volume of liquid will depend on the radius of the sphere (r), the difference in density between the sphere and the liquid $(\Delta\rho)$*, the acceleration of gravity (g) and the viscosity (η). Since we normally express physical properties in terms of only three dimensions, Mass, Length and Time, we must make a further assumption that $\Delta\rho$ and g will have the same power in the equation. This is reasonable, since mass multiplied by acceleration gives the force. (If we had chosen to take four dimensions, including also Force, we need not have made this assumption explicitly.)

We can therefore write:

$$v \propto r^a \quad . \quad \Delta\rho^b \quad . \quad g^b \quad . \quad \eta^c$$
$$LT^{-1} = L^a.(ML^{-3})^b.(LT^{-2})^b.(ML^{-1}T^{-1})^c$$

solving for Mass we get: $0 = b + c$ or $b = -c$
solving for Length we get: $1 = a - 3b + b - 3c$ or $1 = a + b$
solving for Time we get: $-1 = -2b - c$ or $-1 = c$
Hence $c = -1$, $b = +1$ and $a = +2$

Hence the equation reads:

$$V \propto r^2 \Delta\rho g \eta^{-1}$$

Inserting the 2/9 which we have not been able to calculate, we get,

$$v = \frac{2}{9} \frac{r^2 \Delta\rho g}{\eta} \quad \text{which is Stokes' equation.}$$

4/Some other useful equations for Newtonian liquids given without their derivation

Cone-plate rheometer (V.W.)†
   For small angles $= 3\alpha M/2\pi R^3\Omega$
   For larger angles, for a Newtonian
    fluid:

Where M is the torque
α is the angle
R is the radius
Ω is angular velocity

$$M = (4\pi R^3/3)\eta\Omega[\sin\alpha/\cos^2\alpha) - \ln\tan(\pi/4 - \alpha/2)]^{-1}$$

Cone in cone (Höppler)

$$\eta = \frac{Mg3 \sin\left(\dfrac{\beta - \alpha}{2}\right)360t}{4\pi^2 R^3 k\phi}$$

* That it is a *difference* of density follows, not from dimensional theory, but from the Archimedes Principle.
† "V.W." will be used throughout to indicate Van Wazer's book (see Appendix 3).

M = moment (torque)
g = 981 (cgs)
β = outer cone top angle
α = inner cone top angle
t = time (sec)
R = inner cone radius
k = a constant
φ = rotation angle (degrees).

Spheres rolling or sliding in cylindrical tubes.

For large spheres: The velocity (for a Newtonian fluid) increases more or less as the sine of the angle for small angles and the velocity varies inversely as the viscosity (Flowers 1914).

For small spheres: $A\eta v = \frac{4}{3}\pi r^3(\rho_b - \rho_l)g \sin \theta - B\rho_l v^2$

where A and B are constants, to be determined experimentally ($B \sim \frac{1}{2}\pi r^2$)

ρ_b and ρ_l are densities of sphere and liquid respectively

θ is the angle of tilt.

v is velocity of sliding (or rolling)

r is radius of sphere.

(Scott Blair and Oosthuizen 1960.)

Penetrating rod

$$\frac{F}{v} = \frac{2\pi h\eta(R_c^2 + R_b^2)/(R_c^2 - R_b^2)}{\dfrac{(R_c^2 + R_b^2)\ln(R_c/R_b)}{R_c^2 - R_b^2} - 1}$$

where F is applied force

v is velocity of rod

h is height of immersion

R_b is radius of rod

R_c is radius of viscometer.

(V.W. quoted from T. L. Smith *et al.*)

$\left(\text{When } R_c \gg R_b, \text{ we have } \dfrac{F}{v} = \dfrac{2\pi h\eta}{\ln(R_a/R_b) - 1}\right).$

Falling cylinder

For large shear stresses (the simplest condition)

$$\eta = \frac{Wg \ln(b/a)}{2\pi Lv}$$

where W is weight of sinking cylinder
a and b are radii of inner and outer cylindrical rings
L is length of outer cylindrical ring
v is (constant) velocity of fall.
(Dinsdale and Moore, see Appendix 3.)

Penetrating cone (as used for grease and fats)

The yield-value is proportional to the weight of the cone and inversely proportional to a power of the depth of penetration. This power is variously quoted as 2·0 and 1·6 and would appear to depend on the properties of the fat and the exact dimensions of the cone.

Plates sliding parallel to one another

$$\eta = \text{Wght}/Ax$$

where W is applied load
h is film thickness
A is area of plate
x is displacement in time t. (V.W.)

Needle pentrometer

It is empirically found that the viscosity is approximately proportional to the square of the applied pressure.

Compression of tall cylinders and extension of rods

For incompressible materials, the *coefficient of viscous traction* (or compression) is three times the viscosity.* Hence, if F is the compressive or tensile force per unit area, and $\varepsilon = \ln(1/l_0)$ is the Hencky strain, then $\eta = F/3\dot{\varepsilon}$ (Scott Blair and Veinoglou 1943).

Extension of rods under their own weight

$$\eta = \frac{g\rho L_0(1 + 1/l_0)t}{6\ln(1/l_0)}$$

where L_0 is initial length of the rod
l_0 is initial length of an increment of the rod
l is length of increment after flow in time t
ρ is density of liquid.
(Schofield and Scott Blair 1933.)

---

* This is not quite strictly true: see Reiner: "Deformation, Strain and Flow", p. 78 (Appendix 3).

Compression of disks between parallel plates

(a) The case when the liquid initially fills the space between the plates and is extruded from the ends.

$$\eta = 2a^3F/3\pi R^4 \dot{a}$$

where a is the clearance between the plates and $\dot{a}$ its rate of change with time

F is the applied force

R is the radius of the plates

(b) The case where the blob of liquid never completely fills the space between the plates.

$$\eta = 2\pi a^5F/3V^2 \dot{a}$$

where V is volume of sample. (In both cases, $\dot{a}$ is, of course, negative.) (Dienes and Klemm 1946.)

Torsion of rods

$$\eta = \frac{2Wl}{\pi a^4 \omega}$$

where W is torque applied to rod

l is length and a is radius of rod

ω is angular velocity

(Trouton and Andrews 1904.)

Blowing of bubble in material

(Chopin's method, known also as *"ergometer"* and *"alveograph"*).

The equations for the internal pressures, volume and wall thickness of the bubble are given by Bloksma (1957). They are too numerous and complex to be given here. They include Bingham and Maxwell systems as well as Newtonian liquids.

Compression in bulk and triaxial stressing

It has been found that, when soil is compressed in the field by gradually lowering a weight onto its surface, although the shape of the load-deformation curve is complex in detail, for reasonably good tilth, over a considerable range, the deformation is approximately proportional to the square-root of the load.

Soil engineers write an equation $|\tau| = c - \sigma \tan \phi$

where $|\tau|$ is the numerical value of the shear-stress

c is the *cohesion* (i.e. the shear-stress which the material can sustain at zero normal stress)

ϕ is the *angle of friction*.

K*

In triaxial stressing, the formula is:

$$p_2 = 2c \tan \alpha + p_1 \tan^2 \alpha$$

where p_1 is the hydrostatic pressure

p_2 is the normal pressure

α is defined as $45° - \frac{1}{2}\phi$.

(J. C. Jaeger. See Appendix 3.)

The selection of equations for this appendix has been somewhat arbitrary, as was also the choice of methods discussed in the last two chapters. It is hoped, however, that they will give the intending experimenter some ideas in planning his researches into the rheology of complex materials.

For a difficult but very excellent account of the equations for various visco-meters and rheometers, see Oka (1960).

Appendix 3
Books for Further Reading, with Brief Appraisals

Note. Books published before about 1948, and books known to be out of print, are not included. Only English, French and German languages are listed. Books dealing with only one specific material are not generally listed, unless forming part of a series.

Barkas, W. W.—The Swelling of Wood under Stress.
> H.M. Stationery Office (D.S.I.R.), 1949.
> This book covers more than the title suggests. A knowledge of simple calculus is required.

Bergen, J. T. (ed.)—Viscoelasticity: Phenomenological Aspects.
> Academic Press, New York, 1960.
> This is a Symposium held at Lancaster (Pa) 1958. Before about this time, a phenomenological approach to rheology was often criticized as superficial; but it is now appreciated that many materials are so complex that theories involving molecular structure are for the present impossible. The book is valuable but the style is sometimes so involved as to make it difficult to read.

Bowden, F. P. and Tabor, D.—The Friction and Lubrication of Solids.
> Clarendon Press, Oxford, 1954.
> This is the classical source of information on what is now called "Tribology".

Bruyne, N. A. de. and Houwink, R. (eds.)—Adhesion and Adhesives.
> Elsevier, London, 1951.
> The best standard textbook on this subject.

Centre National de la Recherche Scientifique, Paris, 1961.
> Phénomènes de Relaxation et de Fluage en Rhéologie Non-Linéaire, Paris, 1961.
> (No Editor's name given. Introduction by R. Thiry.)
> Proceedings of an International Colloquium. Very high standard but definitely for advanced readers (in French).

Copley, A. L. and Stainsby, G. (eds.)—Flow Properties of Blood and Other Biological Systems.

Pergamon Press, Oxford, 1960.

Proceedings of a Discussion organized jointly by the Faraday Society and the British Society of Rheology, in Oxford in 1959. Covers many aspects of the subject.

Copley, A. L. (ed.)—Proceedings of the First International Conference on Hemorheology, Reykjavik, 1966.

Pergamon Press, Oxford, 1968.

This is a verbatim account of the Proceedings, including all Discussions. It is a "must" for anyone working on flow or coagulation of blood or on the structure of blood vessels and it includes many papers on the physiology of the circulatory system.

Dinsdale, A. and Moore, F.—Viscosity and its Measurement.

Inst. of Physics Monogr., 1962.

It is because this book is available that I have made the experimental part of the present book quite short. This is an excellent little book (only 60 pp.) for beginners who want to know something about standard methods of measuring viscosity. Only quite simple mathematics.

Eirich, F. R. (ed.)—Rheology: Theory and Applications. Vol. 1, 1956: Vol. 2, 1958: Vol. 3, 1960: Vol. 4, 1967 (other vols. to follow).

Academic Press, New York.

A series of essays on almost all aspects of rheology except biorheology. The standard naturally varies but, on the whole, the level is very high. Perhaps, if on a desert island, one were allowed only one book on rheology (in several volumes!) this would be the best choice.

Feltham, P.—Deformation and Strength of Materials.

Butterworth, London, 1966.

Somewhat similar to Reiner's "Lectures" and Jaeger's "Elasticity" (q.v.) but less difficult. Contains an interesting section of metals (the author's speciality) and a discussion on Weissenberg Effects and elastic liquids.

Frey-Wyssling, A. (ed.)—Deformation and Flow in Biological Systems (Monographs on Rheology).

North Holland Publishing Company, Amsterdam, 1952.

Probably the first book of essays on Biorheology, this work covers protoplasm, movement of solutes in plants, animals and man, cerebro-spinal and intraocular fluids, cervical secretions, sinovial fluids and mucins, and diffusion phenomena in biology.

Green, A. E. and Zerna, W.—Theoretical Elasticity.
> Clarendon Press, Oxford, 1954.
> There are many books on the theory of elasticity. None of them is easy reading. This book may be taken as fairly representative.

Green, H.—The Molecular Theory of Fluids (Monographs on Rheology).
> North Holland Publishing Company, Amsterdam, 1952.
> A scholarly essay but recommended only for those able to cope with quite difficult mathematics.

Gross, B.—Mathematical Structure of the Theories of Visco-Elasticity.
> Hermann et Cie, Paris, 1953.
> An admirable summary for advanced readers (in English).

Hermans, J. J. (ed.)—Flow Properties of Disperse Systems (Monographs on Rheology).
> North Holland Publishing Company, Amsterdam, 1953.
> A collection of essays on suspensions, emulsions, gels, foams, smokes and powders, by leading workers in these fields. Not difficult to read.

International Rheology Congresses.
> 1. Scheveningen, 1948 (Organ. Cttee. ed.).
> North Holland Publishing Company, Amsterdam.
> 2. Oxford, 1953 (V. G. W. Harrison ed.).
> Butterworth, London.
> 3. Bad Oehnhausen, 1958.
> Rheol. Acta, Vol. 1, Nos. 2 and 3.
> 4. Providence (R.I.), 1963. (E. H. Lee and A. L. Copley eds.) (4 vols).
> Interscience Publishing, New York.
> 5. Kyoto, 1968 (in process of publication).

Jaeger, J. C.—Elasticity, Fracture and Flow.
> Methuen, London, 1956.
> This is sub-titled "Engineering and Geological Applications". It gives a short but efficient summary of the Theory of Elasticity and deals effectively with problems of strength. It is somewhat condensed (only 149 pp.) and is not easy reading; even though the mathematics is not really very advanced.

Mercier, A.—Leçons et Problèmes sur la Théorie des Corps Déformables.
> Gautier-Villars, Paris, 1953.
> There are not very many French books on rheology. This is one of the best known.

Meredith, R. (ed.)—Mechanical Properties of Wood and Paper (Monographs on Rheology).
North Holland Publishing Company, Amsterdam, 1953.
Ten chapters covering all aspects of the subject.

Meredith, R. (ed.)—Mechanical Properties of Textile Fibres (Monographs on Rheology).
North Holland Publishing Company, Amsterdam, 1956.
Eighteen chapters on all aspects of this subject.

Merrington, A. C.—Viscometry.
Arnold, London, 1949.
A condensed and (when written) up-to-date version of G. Barr's classic "Monograph on Viscometry", this book gives useful accounts of most of the classical methods for measuring viscosity. Equations are given but not always very fully explained.

Mill, C. C. (ed.)—Rheology of Disperse Systems.
Pergamon Press, Oxford, 1959.
The Proceedings of a Conference of the British Society of Rheology (Swansea, 1957). All aspects of the subject are covered. Not difficult mathematics.

Nadai, A.—Theory of Flow and Fracture of Solids.
McGraw-Hill, New York, 1950.
A very sound but difficult book—not to be recommended for beginners.

Nelkon, M.—Mechanics and Properties of Matter.
Heinemann, London, 1952.
Anyone concerned with rheology who is not a physicist should have a book on general mechanical properties. This is a useful example: no difficult mathematics.

Ory, Anne-Marie—Über die rheologischen Eigenschaften einiger Schleim-stoffe und deren Mischungen.
City Druck A. G., Zürich, 1962.
A doctorate thesis on the rheology of mucoid substances, gums, etc. Useful for pharmacy students interested in rheology (in German).

Persoz, B. (ed.)—Introduction à l'Etude de la Rhéologie.
Dunod, Paris, 1960.
An admirable series of Essays but an "Introduction" only for those already competent in mathematics (in French).

Reiner, M. (ed.)—Building Materials: Their Elasticity and Inelasticity (Monographs on Rheology).

North Holland Publishing Company, Amsterdam, 1954.
The first part concerns theoretical, physical, chemical and engineering aspects. The second part deals with metals and wood: the third, with concretes and asphalt: the fourth, with soils, earth and clay and the fifth with minor materials of building construction.

Reiner, M.—Deformation, Strain and Flow (revised edn.).
H. K. Lewis, London, 1960.
Described as "an elementary introduction", this admirable work is considerably more advanced than the present book. But it can be read by most people who have a general knowledge of calculus. (It is believed that a further revised edition is pending.)

Reiner, M.—Lectures on Theoretical Rheology (3rd. edn.).
North Holland Publishing Company, Amsterdam, 1960.
Based on lectures given some years ago, this is by far the simplest introduction to tensor theory as applied to rheology. But the reader must be prepared to work hard!

Scott Blair, G. W. (ed.)—Foodstuffs: their Plasticity, Fluidity and Consistency (Monographs on Rheology).
North Holland Publishing Company, Amsterdam, 1953.
The title reflects the unfortunate decision not to include the word "Rheology" in the title of any of this series of Monographs! Materials dealt with are: starch, cereals, dairy products, confectionery, jellies and syrups. The concluding chapter (by R. Harper) is on "Psycho-rheology of Foodstuffs".

Sherman, P. (ed.)—Rheology of Emulsions.
Pergamon Press, Oxford, 1963.
Proceedings of a Symposium of the British Society of Rheology, Harrogate, 1962. So little work had been done on emulsions at this time, that even this small volume includes much not included in the title. But most of the pages are well worth reading.

Sherman, P.—Emulsion Science.
Academic Press, London and New York, 1968.
The author is a leading authority on emulsions and only one chapter is on rheology. This is, however, the best review yet published and includes almost all relevant references. Some mathematical knowledge is required.

Society of Chemical Industry Monograph No. 7, 1960.
Papers read at a Symposium (1958) on Texture in Foods, this has

interesting chapters on (*inter alia*) bread, chocolate, eggs, fish, meat, peas, potatoes and confectioneries of various kinds.

Treloar, L. R. G.—The Physics of Rubber Elasticity. (2nd edn.)
Oxford University Press, 1958.
This is the standard work on rubber elasticity and, considering the complexity of the subject, it is not very difficult reading.

Van Wazer, J. R., Lyons, J. W., Kim, K. Y. and Colwell, R.E.—Viscosity and Flow Measurement.
Interscience Publishing, New York, 1963.
Rheological studies advance so quickly that this book is already somewhat out of date. But it gave an extensive and excellent list of techniques available for rheologists and full descriptions of many (mostly American) commercially available instruments, together with their formulae when available.

Whitmore, R. L.—The Rheology of the Circulation.
Pergamon Press, Oxford, 1968.
This book covers: "rheological concepts; the circulatory system; the flow of fluids; viscometry; rheology of plasma and blood; dynamics of the circulation; flow of blood in tubes; flow in complex situations; abnormalities of the circulation". It has a bibliography of some 400 references. There is no difficult mathematics.

Wilkinson, W. L.—Non-Newtonian Fluids.
Pergamon Press, Oxford, 1960.
The author is not very familiar with this book but it is often quoted.

References

Andrade, E. N. da C., (1910) *Proc. R. Soc.* (A) **84,** 1.
Andrade, E. N. da C., (1914) *Proc. R. Soc.* (A) **90,** 329.
Andrade, E. N. da C., (1948) *Proc. phys. Soc. Lond.* **60,** 304.
Arnstein, A. and Reiner, M., (1945–Sept.) *Civ. Engng* **3.**
Bailey, R. W., (1932) *Proc. Instn. mech. Engrs* **122,** 281.
Bailey, R. W., (1935) *Proc. Instn. mech. Engrs* **131,** 78, 131
Barnett, C. H., Davies, D. V. and MacConaill, M. A., (1961) "Synovial Joints: their Structure and Mechanics", Longmans Green, London, p. 74.
Bauer, W. H. and Collins, E. A., (1967) "Rheology: Theory and Applications", Ed. F. R. Eirich, Academic Press, New York, vol. **4,** p. 423.
Behar, Y. and Frei, E. H., (1955) *Bull. Res. Coun. Israel* **5A,** 82.
Bell, G. H., (1956) "The Biochemistry and Physiology of Bone", Ed. G. H. Bourne, Academic Press, New York.
Bergel, D. H., (1966) *Lab. Pract.* **15,** 77.
Bloksma, A. H., (1957) *Cereal Chem.* **34,** 126.
Burgers, J. M. and Scott Blair, G. W., (1949) "Report on the Principles of Rheological Nomenclature", North Holland Publishing Company, Amsterdam.
Burnett, J., Glover, F. A. and Scott Blair, G. W., (1967) *Biorheol.* **4,** 41.
Caffyn, J. E., (1944) *J. scient. Instrum.* **21,** 213.
Clift, A. F., (1947) *Br. med. J.* **4489,** 113.
Clift, A. F., Glover, F. A. and Scott Blair, G. W., (1950) *Lancet* **i,** p. 1154.
Clift, A. F. and Hart, J., (1953) *J. Physiol.* **122,** 358.
Conway, B. E. and Dobry-Duclaux, A., (1960) "Rheology: Theory and Applications", Ed. F. R. Eirich, Academic Press, New York, vol. **3.** 82.
Copley, A. L., Scott Blair, G. W., Glover, F. A. and Thorley, R. S., (1960) *Kolloid Zeit.* **168,** 101.
Criddle, D. W., (1960) "Rheology: Theory and Applications", Ed. F. R. Eirich, Academic Press, New York, vol. **4,** p. 429.
Currey, J. D., (1964) *Biorheol.* **2,** 1.
Dienes, G. H. and Klemm, H. F., (1946) *J. appl. Phys.* **17,** 458.
Dingle, H., (1949) *Phil. Mag.* **40,** 94.
Dorn, J. E., (1956) "Creep and Fracture of Metals" (N.P.L. Symposium 1954), H.M.S.O., London.
Dorn, J. E., Goldberg, A. and Tietz, T. E., (1948) *Trans. Inst. Mi. metall. Engrs* **15,** T.P. 2445.
Drake, B, (1962) *J. Fd. Sci.* **27,** 192.
Drake, B., (1963) *J. Fd. Sci.* **28,** 233.
Drake, B., (1965) *Biorheol.* **3,** 21.
Edsall, J. T., (1942) "Advances in Colloid Science", Interscience Publishers, Inc., New vol **1,** p. 269.

Eirich. F. R. (Ed.) "Rheology: Theory and Practice". Academic Press, New York, vol. **1** (1956), vol. **2** (1958), vol. **3** (1960), vol. **4** (1967).

Eliassaf, J., Silberberg, A. and Katchalsky, A., (1955) *Nature, Lond.* **176**, 1119.

Fåhraeus, R. and Lindquist, T., (1931) *Am. J. Physiol.* **96**, 562.

Flowers, A. E., (1914) *Proc. Am. Soc. Test. Mater.* **14**, 565.

Ford, T. F., (1960) *J. phys. Chem. Wash.*, **64**, 1168.

Gent, A. N., (1960) *Br. J. appl. Phys.* **11**, 85.

Glasstone, S., Laidler, K. J. and Eyring, H., (1941) "Theory of Rate Processes". McGraw-Hill, New York.

Glover, F. A. and Scott Blair, G. W., (1956) *Biorheol.* **3**, 189.

Goldsmith, H. L. and Mason, S. G., (1961) *Nature, Lond.* **190**, 1095.

Goldsmith, H. L. and Mason, S. G., (1962) *Proc. 2nd Int. Conf. Microcirculation (Pavia)* p. 462.

Graham, A., (1952) *Engineer, Lond.*, **193**, 198, 234.

Graham A., (1957) *9th Int. Conf. appl. Mech. Brussels* **8**, 227.

Graham, A. and Walles, K. F. A., (1958) *Aeron. Res. Conn.* Current Paper CP 379, 380 (H.M.S.O.).

Graham, A., (1960) *Cah. Grpe fr. Étud. Rhéol.* **5**, 213.

Graham, A., (1967) *Engineer, Lond.*, **223**, 192.

Grant, N. J. and Bucklin, A. G., (1950) *Trans. Am. Soc. Metals* **42**, 720.

Harkness, J., (1963) *Lancet*, **ii**, p. 280.

Harper, R. and Stevens, S. S., (1964) *Q. Jl. exp. Psychol.* **16.**, 204.

Hartert, H., (1952) *Germ. Pat. Specn.* No. 845720.

Hartert, H. and Schaeder, J. A., (1962) *Biorheol.* **1**, 31.

Harvey, C. and Jackson, M. H., (1948) *Lancet*, **ii**, p. 723.

Harvey, C., (1954) *J. Obstet. Gynaec. Br. Commonw.* **61**, 480.

Harvey, C., Linn, R. A. and Jackson, M. H., (1960) *J. Reprod. Fert.* **1**, 157.

Heilbrunn, L. V., (1958) *Protoplasmatologia* **2.**

Heilbrunn, L. V., (1960) "Flow Properties of Blood and other Biological Systems", Eds. A. L. Copley and G. Stainsby, Pergamon Press, Oxford, p. 327.

Herschel, W. H. and Bulkley, R., (1926) *Kolloid Zeit.* **39**, 291.

Hinshelwood, C. N., (1952) "The Structure of Physical Chemistry", Oxford University Press.

Hollomon, J. H., (1947) *Trans. Am. Inst. Mi. metall. Engrs* **171**, 535.

Jeffery, G. B., (1922) *Proc. R. Soc.* (A) **107**, 161.

Joly, M., (1966) *Biorheol.* **4**, 11.

Johns, R. J. and Wright, V., (1964) *Biorheol.* **2**, 87.

Juliusburger, F. and Pirquet, A., (1936) *Trans. Faraday Soc.* **32**, 445.

Kamiya, N., (1959) *Protoplasmatologia* **8.**

Katchalsky, A., Kedem, O., Klibansky, C. and de Vries, A., (1960) "Flow Properties of Blood and Other Biological Systems", Eds. A. L. Copley and G. Stainsby, Pergamon Press, Oxford, p. 155.

Katz, D., (1937) *Cereal Chem.* **14**, 382.

Landau, C. S., (1959) *Br. J. appl. Phys.* **10**, 476.

Ludwick, P., (1909) "Elemente der Technologische Mechanik", J. Springer, Berlin.

MacGregor, C. W. and Fisher, J. C., (1946) *J. appl. Mech.* **13A**, 11.

MacGregor, C. W. and Fisher, J. C., (1945) *J. appl. Mech.* **12A**, 217.

Mardles, E. W. J., (1946) *Nature, Lond.* **158**, 199.

Marvin, R. S., (1952) *Ind. Engng Chem. ind. (int.) Edn* **44**, 696.

Matz, S. A., (1962) "Food Texture", Avi Publishing Company, Westport, Conn., U.S.A.,

Myers, R. R., Negami, S. and White, R. K., (1966) *Biorheol.* **3**, 197.

Nutting, P. G., (1921) *Proc. Am. Soc. Test. Mater.* **21**, 1162.

Nutting, P. G., (1946) *J. Franklin Inst.* **242**, 449.

Oka, S., (1960) "Rheology: Theory and Applications", Ed. F. R. Eirich, Academic Press, New York, vol. **3**, p. 17.

Orowan, E., (1947) *J. W. Scotl. Iron Steel Inst.* **54**, 45.

Reiner, M., (1963) *Proc. 4th Int. Congr. Rheol.* **1**, 267.

Roscoe, R. (1950) *Br. J. appl. Phys.* **1**, 171.

Roscoe, R., (1952) *Br. J. appl. Phys.* **3**, 267.

Rutgers, R., (1962) *Rheol. Acta.* **2**, 305.

Saunders, B., (1948) *J. Oil Colour Chem. Ass.* **31**, 95.

Schofield, R. K. and Scott Blair, G. W., (1930) *J. phys. Chem., Ithaca* **34**, 1505.

Schofield, R. K. and Scott Blair, G. W., (1933) *Proc. R. Soc.* (A) **139**, 557.

Scott Blair, G. W., (1931) *Trans. Ceram. Soc.* **30**, 138.

Scott Blair, G. W. and Coppen, F. M. V., (1939) *Proc. R. Soc.* (B) **128**, 109.

Scott Blair, G. W. and Veinoglou, B. C., (1943) *J. scient. Instrum.* **20**, 58.

Scott Blair, G. W., Veinoglou, B. C. and Caffyn, J. E., (1947) *Proc. R. Soc.* (A) **189**, 69.

Scott Blair, G. W. and Caffyn, J. E., (1949) *Phil. Mag.* **40**, 80.

Scott Blair, G. W., (1949) "A Survey of General and Applied Rheology", 2nd edn. Pitman, London.

Scott Blair, G. W., (1950) "Some Recent Developments in Rheology", Ed. V. G. W. Harrison, United Trade Press, London, p. 105.

Scott Blair, G. W., (1952) "Deformation and Flow in Biological Systems", Ed. A. Frey-Wyssling, North Holland Publishing Company, Amsterdam, p. 447.

Scott Blair, G. W. and Glover, F., (1957) *Br. vet. J.* **113**, 417.

Scott Blair, G. W., (1958a) *Research, Lond.* **11**, 123.

Scott Blair, G. W., (1958b) *Rheol. Acta.* **1**, 123.

Scott Blair, G. W. and Burnett, J., (1959) *Br. J. appl. Phys.* **10**, 97.

Scott Blair, G. W., (1960) "Flow Properties of Blood and Other Biological Systems", Eds. A. L. Copley and G. Stainsby, Pergamon Press, Oxford, p. 172.

Scott Blair, G. W. and Burnett, J., (1960) *Kolloid Zeit.* **168**, 98.

Scott Blair, G. W. and Oosthuizen, J. C., (1960) *Br. J. appl. Phys.* **11**, 332.

Scott Blair, G. W., (1967) *Rheol. Acta.* **6**, 201.

Scott Blair, G. W. and Burnett, J., (1968) *Biorheol.* **5**, 163.

Segrè, G. and Silberberg, A., (1961) *Nature, Lond.* **189**, 209.

Signer, R., (1954) "Physical Methods and Organic Chemistry", Ed. A. Weissberger, Interscience Publishers Inc., New York, p. 2225.

Soderberg, C. R., (1936) *Trans. Am. Soc. mech. Engrs* **58**, 733.

Stevens, S. S., (1951) "Handbook of Experimental Psychology", Chapman and Hall, London, Chapter 1.

Stevens, S. S., (1957) *Psychol. Rev.* **64**, 153.

Stevens, S. S. and Guirao, M., (1964) *Science, N.Y.* **144**, 1157.

Szczesniak, A. S., (1963) *Fd Res.* **28**, 385, 397.

Tabor, D., (1956) *Br. J. appl. Phys.* **7**, 159.

148   REFERENCES

Taylor, G. I., (1932) *Proc. R. Soc.* (A) **138,** 41.
Taylor, G. I., (1936) *Proc. R. Soc.* (A) **157,** 546, 565.
Treisman, M., (1962) *Br. J. Phil. Sci.* **13,** 130.
Trouton, F. T. and Andrews, E. S., (1904) *Phil. Mag.* **7,** 347.
Trouton, F. T., (1906) *Proc. R. Soc.* (A) **77,** 426.
Walles, K. F. A. and Tilly, G. P., (1967) *Engineer, Lond.* **224,** 551.
Weissenberg, K., (1949) *Proc. 1st Int. Congr. Rheol.,* North Holland Publishing Company, Amsterdam.
White, J. C. and Elmes, P. C., (1960) "Rheology of Blood and Other Biological Systems". Eds. A. L. Copley and G. Stainsby, Pergamon Press, Oxford, p. 259.
Willets, W. R., (1967) *Physics to-day* **20,** 11.
Zener, (C.) and Hollomon, J. H., (1944) *Trans. Am. Soc. Metals* **33,** 188.

Indexes

Author Index

Numbers in italics refer to the section in which the full reference is given.

151

Subject Index

Numbers in italics refer to definitions and explanations of terms. References from Appendix 3 are not included.